elements of General Topology

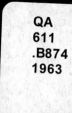
elements of

General Topology

a.o15s

D. Bushaw

PROFESSOR OF MATHEMATICS, WASHINGTON STATE UNIVERSITY

John Wiley & Sons, Inc., New York · London

preface

Several important branches of modern mathematics depend heavily on the young but fundamental mathematical doctrine variously called general, point set, or set-theoretic topology. The purpose of this book is to provide a brief account of some of the essentials of this subject, and thereby to supply a large share of the prerequisites for the study of the fields that depend on it. In line with this goal, the book puts almost all its emphasis on the absolutely basic concepts, principles, and constructions; even the examples have been chosen so as to produce minimal distraction from the main lines of development.

The student is probably ready to read the book if he has reached or passed the level of mathematical *savoir faire* represented by having taken about three years of sound undergraduate mathematics. The only specific prerequisite is some knowledge of set theory. For those readers who do not have this knowledge there is an appendix that outlines the parts of set theory that the book uses and makes some suggestions about preliminary or complementary reading on the subject.

Study of this book will require the reader's active participation. Many proofs, for example, are only sketched; some are omitted entirely. The descriptive text contains occasional assertions that are really little theorems in themselves, but for which no explicit justification is given. All these omissions are intended as opportunities for him to do some proving on his own; and the process of filling these gaps, if undertaken in the right spirit, should be at least as instructive as the mere reading of what he finds between them. There are also some explicit exercises besides these implicit ones, and answers or hints for some of them appear at the end of the book. The exercises in each group are arranged in approximately increasing order of difficulty, and exceptionally difficult exercises are marked with an asterisk.

When the student has finished this book, he may want to consolidate his gains by doing some reading in an area of mathematics where general topology is put to work. The second appendix contains specific recommendations for further study of this kind, and also for further reading in general topology itself.

Theorems are numbered in one sequence through the book, and the exercises are numbered in another. Russian names are transliterated according to the system used in *Mathematical Reviews*, but any other common transliteration of a name is given in brackets after the first occurrence of that name.

I would like to thank the students whose response to the lecture notes on which this book is based instigated my writing it; and Doctors G. Philip Johnson and H. C. Wiser, for reading the whole manuscript and making many thoughtful suggestions for improvement, most of which I accepted.

Baltimore, Md.   D. Bushaw
June, 1963.

contents

CHAPTER ONE
historical introduction

One of the distinctive characteristics of modern mathematics is its way of taking old mathematical ideas apart like watches, studying the parts separately, putting these parts together again in various new and interesting combinations, and studying these combinations in turn. The real number system provides a good example or, more precisely, a good nexus of examples of the process. The full richness of this familiar system becomes clearer when some of the various ways in which it can be considered are recalled. For instance:

The real number system is an *algebraic* system: It is a set on which certain algebraic operations (most importantly, addition and multiplication) are defined, and these operations have certain basic properties—associativity, commutativity, and so on.

The real number system is an *ordered* system: It is a set on which there is defined an order relation (say $<$), and this relation has certain basic properties—for example, transitivity.

The real number system is a *distanced*, or *metric* system: It is a set to each pair of whose elements there is assigned a number interpreted as the distance between them, and this distance has certain basic properties—for example, the distance between two real numbers is zero if and only if the numbers are equal.

The full interest of the real number system depends not only on these three separate aspects, and on others that might be added to the list, but also on the relations between them. The fundamental fact that, if a, b, and c are any real numbers, and if $a < b$, then $a + c < b + c$ is one property of the real number system in which both the algebraic and the order aspects come into play.

1

Nevertheless, there are advantages in studying the separate aspects of the real number system one at a time. The greatest advantage, perhaps, is a matter of making the best use of the collective effort of mathematicians. If, for example, a theory is worked out for the real number system strictly as an ordered system, this theory not only may improve our understanding of the real number system itself, but also is available for immediate application to any other mathematical system which is like the real number system as regards order, even if in no other respect. In effect, such a theory may take care of the order aspects of many different mathematical objects at once, and relieve mathematicians from the task of going over what amounts to the same line of reasoning again and again.

More generally, by abstracting from familiar mathematical ideas in one or more directions it is possible to develop an arsenal of general theories which serve several purposes: They may improve our understanding of the familiar ideas on which they are based; they equip us with ready-made schemes for the analysis, at least in part, of other familiar mathematical ideas, or entirely new ones; and they are often interesting in themselves. Much of the vigorous mathematical activity of the last few decades has been devoted to the construction and study of general theories of this kind, and for these reasons.

The subject of this book is one of the general theories that arose more or less in this way. An enthusiast, by stretching a point here and there, might extend the history of general topology back to a surprisingly remote date, but there is probably little to be gained by going back beyond the researches of Georg Cantor. Starting about 1870 with some moderately straightforward problems in the theory of Fourier series, Cantor was led to investigate properties of subsets of the real number system and of n-dimensional Euclidean space. These sets were not necessarily intervals, curves, surfaces, polyhedra, and so on, of the familiar kinds but could be very bizarre indeed. To carry out these investigations he not only had to come to grips with the previously evaded concept of the infinite, developing a whole new arithmetic of transfinite numbers, but also introduced and made extensive use of certain new purely distance-related concepts; for example, that of the derivative (*Ableitung*) of a set. He defined the derivative of a set X of points in n-dimensional Euclidean space to be the set of all points x with the property that infinitely many points of X could be found within any arbitrarily small distance of x.

At just about the time when Cantor's own research was tapering off, partly because of vigorous opposition from tradition-bound contemporaries, other mathematicians began to elaborate on and extend the scope of his ideas. Perhaps the most important of his immediate followers in the line that led to general topology were members of an Italian school that included G. Ascoli, V. Volterra, C. Arzelà, and S. Pincherle; in the 1880's they began to apply Cantor's distance-related concepts to "spaces" that were not spaces in the conventional sense at all—for example, "spaces" in which the typical "point" might be a curve or a function.

The next major step was taken by Maurice Fréchet, who made an observation that seems perfectly natural now but was radical for its time. In his doctoral thesis, published in 1906, he suggested that much of the work that had been done and was being done on distance-related concepts in a number of specific "spaces" might be done more economically by considering a single abstract, but appropriately restricted, concept of "distance" defined for pairs of equally abstract "points" and developing its properties once for all. He suggested and explored several alternative ways of doing this, but his most influential proposal was the concept of what is now called a metric space [in Fréchet's original terminology, a class (E)]. A metric space may be described as a nonempty set S together with a function that assigns to any pair of elements x and y of S a real number $d(x, y)$, provided that this function satisfies certain simple conditions, which will not be enumerated here. The number $d(x, y)$ is interpreted as the "distance" between the "points" x and y.

The most familiar spaces of nineteenth-century mathematics—and many other mathematical systems too—can be regarded as specific metric spaces, and naturally any conclusion obtained for metric spaces in general can be applied at once to any of these particular spaces. The list of restrictions on the "distance function" d was shrewdly chosen; it was liberal enough to cover a great variety of important mathematical systems, yet tight enough to provide the basis for a theory within which most of the important distance-related concepts (which included, as it turned out, convergence, continuity, and so on) can be defined in a natural way, and many of the important theorems about them can be proved.

For example, continuity can be defined in a general metric space setting this way: If S with the distance function d, and S' with the distance function d', are metric spaces, and f is a function from S into S', and x is a "point" of S, then f is said to be continuous at x if for any positive real number ϵ there exists a positive real number δ such that $d'[f(x), f(y)] < \epsilon$ if $d(x, y) < \delta$. This can be regarded as a perfectly straightforward restatement of the definition that is found in good calculus textbooks, where S and S' are usually both the real number system, and $d(x, y)$ and $d'(x, y)$ are both given by $|x - y|$. Using only the conditions on distance functions stipulated by Fréchet one can go on from this general definition to prove general metric space counterparts for many fundamental theorems about functions that are continuous in the conventional sense; for example, the theorem that the composite of two continuous functions is continuous. In similar ways, many of the other familiar concepts that depend mainly on distance may be transplanted to general metric space theory with many of their important properties clinging to them. This was done in a number of instances by Fréchet himself.

The process of generalization did not stop with the introduction of metric spaces; within a few years of the publication of Fréchet's thesis, several mathematicians (especially F. Riesz, F. Hausdorff, and Fréchet himself) observed that the distance function was not really needed for most of the purposes served by the concept of a metric space, and that almost everything one wanted to do could be done using some such subsidiary concept as that of a "neighborhood," itself a generalization of an older idea: In a metric space, a (spherical) neighborhood of a point x is the set of all points y satisfying $d(x, y) < \epsilon$, where ϵ is some positive real number called the radius of the neighborhood. The typical spherical neighborhood of a point x in a metric space is accordingly the set of all elements "within a certain distance of" x. Now Hausdorff may speak for himself.*

Now these spherical neighborhoods, as we will call them, have a series of properties of which only a very few are needed at first. Thus . . . we change our viewpoint by disregarding the distances by means of which we defined neighborhoods, and put those properties at the head as axioms.

By a *topological* space we mean a set S in which certain subsets U_x, which we call neighborhoods, are assigned to the elements (points), and in fact according to the following

Neighborhood Axioms

(A) To each point x there corresponds at least one neighborhood; every neighborhood U_x has x as an element.

(B) If U_x and V_x are two neighborhoods of the same point x, there exists a neighborhood W_x of x such that $W_x \subset U_x \cap V_x$.

(C) If $y \in U_x$, there exists a neighborhood U_y such that $U_y \subset U_x$.

* This passage is translated, in language and notation, from Hausdorff's *Grundzüge der Mengenlehre*, Veit, Leipzig, 1914; reprinted, Chelsea, New York, 1949; p. 213.

(D) For any two distinct points x, y there exist two disjoint neighborhoods U_x, U_y.*

It is not hard to show that the spherical neighborhoods in a metric space do satisfy Hausdorff's "neighborhood axioms"; so every metric space may be regarded as a "topological space"; but the latter concept is more general. Despite this greater generality, however, much of the theory of metric spaces (and therefore of distance-related aspects of many specific spaces) can be moved almost intact into the new setting. A brief return to the idea of continuity will illustrate the point. The definition of continuity already given for functions from one metric space into another may be readily paraphrased to read: f is continuous at x if, for every neighborhood U_y (in S') of $y = f(x)$ there exists a neighborhood U_x of x such that $f(u) \in U_y$ if $u \in U_x$. This statement, however, unlike the previous one, has meaning if the spaces involved are merely topological spaces in Hausdorff's sense, and may therefore be taken as a definition of continuity for functions from one topological space into another. Here again, the definition and the "neighborhood axioms" are of such a nature that natural counterparts of many classical theorems about continuity can be proved at this more general level.

The advantages of the topological space concept over the metric space concept depend on more than a principle of generality for the sake of generality. The first successes of the program of isolating certain originally distance-related mathematical concepts in one theory made it natural to hope and expect that this theory might ultimately lie at a very fundamental level in the structure of mathematics as a whole and presuppose only such still more fundamental theories as set theory and its logical prerequisites. A distance function, however, is a function into the real number system, and some of the most essential parts of metric space theory—the proof of the fact that neighborhoods in a metric space satisfy Hausdorff's axioms (A)–(D), for example—depend heavily on properties of the real number system. Thus any attempt to put metric space theory ahead of the theory of real numbers on the scale of increasing logical priority would necessarily lead to circularity. The transition to Hausdorff's concept of a topological space, which did not depend on the theory of real num-

* For the set theory symbols used here, see *Sets*, 1, 5, 9. A reference written *Sets*, z is to the paragraph or paragraphs numbered z in Appendix 1. A reader who is already acquainted with the terms, symbols, or formulas to which such a reference is attached can ignore it.

bers or on any other more special mathematical constructs, removed this difficulty and made it possible for the young theory to be put, uncontaminated, in its proper place.

The introduction of topological spaces was therefore a most satisfactory step forward. At one stroke, it simplified the theory, widened its scope, and made it as mathematically self-contained as could be expected. This makes it easy to understand the rapid shift in interest, in the years immediately following 1914, from metric space theory to general topology, the theory of topological spaces.

There was nevertheless a certain price to be paid for this progress. The successive generalizations preserved many of the features of the original systems, but not all; and useful things were sometimes among the casualties. For instance, it is a routine matter to define the important concept of uniform continuity for functions from one metric space into another, but there is no adequate way of carrying this concept over into the theory of topological spaces in general. Some of these limitations led, especially in the 1930's, to partial retreats from the level of generality occupied by Hausdorff's and other definitions of a topological space.

Some major improvements in Hausdorff's definition were not in the direction of less generality. Many substitutes for the Hausdorff definition have been proposed, and several still have their respective groups of followers. The definition adopted in this book (and elsewhere) looks very different from Hausdorff's, but in the upshot is equivalent to what Hausdorff's definition would be without axiom (D), which has proved to be a little too restrictive. This matter will be discussed in some detail in the proper place.

Developments in the theory of topological spaces since 1914 have not been confined to skirmishes about definitions, however, and much has been done to enrich, expand, and refine the theory itself. It would be inappropriate to give here a detailed account, or even a moderately complete sketch, of the history of these developments, but a few of the major milestones may be mentioned.

First in historical order was the establishment, in 1920, of the periodical *Fundamenta Mathematicae*, published in Warsaw. The publication of this journal was part of a program for the rejuvenation of Polish mathematics outlined by Z. Janiszewski, who had suggested that the growth of a strong mathematical tradition in postwar Poland might best be furthered by choosing one or two fields in which to concentrate at first. Happily for general topology, one field chosen for this role was the infant theory of topological spaces, and *Fundamenta*

Mathematicae was especially hospitable to contributions to this theory. The program was strikingly successful, leading to the rise of a strong school of Polish topologists that included W. Sierpiński, C. Kuratowski, and many others; and it provided topologists all over the world with what was to a large extent their own journal.

Shortly after *Fundamenta* began to appear, heightened interest in algebraic topology (also called combinatorial topology or *analysis situs*), which used general topology as a tool, led to a sharpening of this tool, and many of the developments in general topology since the early 1920's have been motivated by the needs of algebraic topology. Similarly, an accelerating interest in topological groups—that is, algebraic groups which are also topological spaces, the algebraic and topological aspects being required to be compatible in certain ways—and in other topological algebraic systems put demands on general topology which were met by the introduction of new ideas and the elaboration of older ones.

It may be legitimate to say that the confluence of general topology with algebra has culminated in modern functional analysis, the subject toward which Pincherle, Fréchet, and others had been moving at the turn of the century.

A number of problems within general topology itself acted as foci of interest and activity in the subject. One of the most famous of these was the so-called metrization problem. Although every metric space is automatically a topological space, it has long been recognized that not all topological spaces can be regarded as metric spaces: there are topological spaces in which the neighborhoods could not possibly be specified in terms of a distance function. The metrization problem was that of finding purely topological conditions under which a topological space could be regarded as a metric space. The first major work on this problem was done by some Russian mathematicians, including P. S. Aleksandrov [Alexandroff] and P. Uryson [Urysohn], but it soon began to receive international attention. The first satisfactory solutions were finally obtained in the 1950's. They are not described in this book, but some of the ideas that emerged as by-products of the long struggle with the problem have acquired independent importance and will be presented in subsequent chapters.

The years 1935–1940 were notably fruitful for general topology. It was in this period that the concept of convergence in topological spaces began to be clarified by use of the new, and more or less equivalent, theories of nets and filters; the theory of compactifications (that is, extensions of a given topological space that have the important property called "compactness") began to take something like definitive shape; and the useful concept of a uniform space, less general than that of a topological space but more general than that of a metric space, was introduced.

It was also in these years that a group of mathematicians writing under the whimsical collective name of N. Bourbaki began issuing instalments of their compendious *Éléments de mathématique*, with general topology as the subject of Book III of this treatise. Besides giving an account of general topology that will probably be accepted as more or less definitive for some time to come, Bourbaki, by putting the section on topology so early in the treatise—preceded only by Book I on set theory and Book II on algebra—forcibly reminded the mathematical world that when contemporary mathematics is organized in a logically (not necessarily pedagogically or historically) suitable order general topology belongs at a very basic level indeed.

Since 1940 the research in general topology has continued to be abundant, and although many of the primary problems have been satisfactorily settled, it is still a living and evolving branch of mathematics. For the student who regards his study of general topology as a preliminary to other studies, however—and it is for him that this book is mainly intended—general topology already provides a supple and far-ranging collection of information and insights.

CHAPTER TWO

fundamentals

Prelude. It has already been mentioned that a definition of topological spaces different from Hausdorff's will be the starting point for the theory developed in this book. It is now the most widely used definition and is therefore the best one to adopt in an introductory account of the subject; moreover, there are good reasons for its being widely used.

Nevertheless, since something has been said about the historical background of Hausdorff's definition, it may be worthwhile to give some indication of the relationship between the two. This will perhaps make it easier to accept the newer definition, whose sudden appearance might otherwise seem disconcertingly abrupt.

The discussion that follows is in general terms, but it will help to keep a specific example in mind. A simple example, and in some ways the classical example, is obtained by taking as S the set of all points on some straight line, and taking as the typical neighborhood of some point x the set of all points on the line whose distances from x are less than some positive number. It is easy to check that these neighborhoods satisfy Hausdorff's four axioms (p. 4)—see the figure—so that the construction gives a topological space in Hausdorff's sense of the term.

By definition, a set X in any such space is *open* if, for every point x that belongs to X, the set X contains a neighborhood U_x of x. On the line, for example, any set obtained by removing a single point from S is open.

Open sets behave very much like neighborhoods. Indeed, they *are* neighborhoods in the sense that if the original neighborhoods are dis-

9

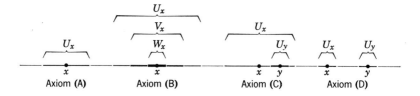

carded and the term "neighborhood of x" is now taken to mean "open set to which x belongs," then Hausdorff's four axioms are still satisfied. Moreover, since each of the original neighborhoods is an open set (see Exercise 3), these new "neighborhoods" include the original ones.

Thus, for any given topological space it is possible to define a second topological space with the same set S but with new and normally different neighborhoods, namely the open sets of the original topological space. The upshot is that the two topological spaces, while not in general formally identical, are the same for all practical purposes. In other words, as far as the ultimate results and applications are concerned, it makes not the slightest difference which system of neighborhoods is chosen: the original neighborhoods, or the open-set neighborhoods. This is not an assertion that can be adequately defended in a few sentences, but its truth will emerge as the development in subsequent sections unfolds.

At the level of convenience, however, there are differences; and these differences are usually all in favor of the second system of neighborhoods. Both systems, of course, have the important properties expressed by the four Hausdorff axioms, but the open-set neighborhoods always have several further properties that make them particularly easy to work with. Four of these further properties are paramount.

First, *S itself is open*. If $x \in S$, then according to axiom (A) there exists a neighborhood U_x of x, and U_x is certainly contained in S. Thus S meets the requirement for being open.

Second, *the empty set $\emptyset$ is open (Sets, 4)*. This particular open set can never be a neighborhood, because no point belongs to it, but it must be counted among the open sets nevertheless. If $\emptyset$ were not open, there would have to be some point x belonging to $\emptyset$ of which $\emptyset$ contained no neighborhood; but this is impossible, because $\emptyset$ has no elements at all.

Third, *the union of any collection of open sets is open* (*Sets*, 10). If $\mathcal{U}$ is any collection of open sets, and $x \in \cup \mathcal{U}$, then by the definition of the union there is some set U belonging to $\mathcal{U}$ such that $x \in U$. Since U is open by assumption, U contains a neighborhood U_x of x. Then $U_x \subset \cup \mathcal{U}$ because $U \subset \cup \mathcal{U}$. This shows that $\cup \mathcal{U}$ contains a neighborhood of any of its points and consequently is open.

Fourth, *the intersection of any nonempty finite collection of open sets is open* (*Sets*, 2). The word "nonempty" appears here simply because the intersection of the empty collection is not defined. The word "finite" appears for an equally good reason: Without it, the statement would be false. For example, in the line the intersection of the collection of all neighborhoods of a point x is just the singleton set $\{x\}$ of that point (*Sets*, 8). Every neighborhood is open (see Exercise 3), but it is easy to see that the set $\{x\}$ is not—it contains no neighborhood of x. To prove the italicized statement, let $\{U_1, \ldots, U_n\}$ be a finite collection of open sets, and let $x \in U_1 \cap \cdots \cap U_n$. For each k between 1 and n inclusive, $x \in U_k$. Since U_k is open, it contains a neighborhood $U_{x,k}$ of x. By axiom (A),

$$x \in U_{x,1} \cap \cdots \cap U_{x,n} \subset U_1 \cap \cdots \cap U_n.$$

(*Sets*, 13). It follows from axiom (B) (see Exercise 4) that the first intersection in this display contains a neighborhood of x; so this neighborhood is contained in $U_1 \cap \cdots \cap U_n$, which is therefore open.

The remarkable thing about these four properties is that they embody the essence of the open-set concept. For an extremely wide variety of purposes, all that has to be known about open sets is that they have these four properties.

Because of the distinct superiority of the open-set neighborhoods, it is natural to consider abandoning the old definition of a topological space altogether, and to thrust the open sets into the forefront. More precisely, instead of defining a topological space as a set S with certain "neighborhoods" that satisfy suitable conditions (the four Hausdorff axioms), the mathematician might define a topological space as a set S with certain "open sets" that satisfy conditions suitable for them (the four properties enumerated above). This is exactly what is done. The definition of a topological space that appears at the beginning of the next section is just such a definition, only more carefully stated. Later the neighborhood concept will reappear, but in a somewhat altered form and in a definitely subordinate role. Hausdorff's definition of a topological space is at last allowed to withdraw to the respected place in the limbo of mathematical history where it belongs.

Exercises. In these four exercises "topological space" should be taken in Hausdorff's sense.

1. Show that it is possible to make the set S of points on a line into a topological space by assigning to each point x just one neighborhood, namely the singleton $\{x\}$. What sets are open in this space?

2. Verify in detail that the open sets in any topological space satisfy Hausdorff's axioms in the way described in the text.

3. Show that every neighborhood in a topological space is open.

4. Show that in a given topological space the intersection of any nonempty finite collection of neighborhoods of a point x contains a neighborhood of x.

Topologies and Topological Spaces. If S is a nonempty set, a collection $\mathfrak{I}$ of subsets of S is called a *topology on* S if it meets the following requirements:

$\qquad$ (O_1) The union of any subcollection of $\mathfrak{I}$ belongs to $\mathfrak{I}$.

$\qquad$ (O_2) The intersection of any nonempty finite subcollection of $\mathfrak{I}$ belongs to $\mathfrak{I}$.

$\qquad$ (O_3) $S \in \mathfrak{I}$.

An ordered pair $(S, \mathfrak{I})$ in which the first component, S, is a nonempty set, and the second component, $\mathfrak{I}$, is a topology on S, is called a *topological space*. The set S is called its *ground set*, and the elements of S are called its *points*. A subset of S is said to be *open* when it belongs to $\mathfrak{I}$, and only then. The use of an ordered pair here is a neat and adequate way of encompassing the idea that is often expressed less rigorously by saying that a topological space is a set with an associated topology, or a set certain of whose subsets are called "open," or other words to the same general effect. It is still common to put the emphasis on S, even to the point of using such phrases as "a topological space S"; but it must be remembered that a set S by itself is not a topological space, nor does it uniquely determine a topological space of which it is the ground set—unless it has only one element! Certain sets are ordinarily endowed with certain standard topologies, and in such cases the abbreviated terminology is relatively safe.

$\qquad$ It is sometimes convenient to compare topologies on a given nonempty set S by using the inclusion relation: If $\mathfrak{I}_1$ and $\mathfrak{I}_2$ are topologies on S, and $\mathfrak{I}_1 \subset \mathfrak{I}_2$, then $\mathfrak{I}_1$ is said to be *coarser* than $\mathfrak{I}_2$; alternatively, $\mathfrak{I}_2$ is said to be *finer* than $\mathfrak{I}_1$.

$\qquad$ The condition (O_3) asserts that the ground set of any topological space is one of its open sets. If (O_1) is applied to the empty sub-collection of $\Im$, one finds also that the empty set $\emptyset$, as the union of this collection, is also open. The pair $\{\emptyset, S\}$, which is therefore contained in any topology on S, is in fact a topology itself. It is called the *trivial* topology on S, and it is clearly coarser than any topology on S. At the other extreme is the power set $\mathcal{P}(S)$ (*Sets*, 5), which certainly satisfies (O_1)–(O_3) and is therefore a topology on S. Finer than any topology on S, it is called the *discrete* topology. These two extreme topologies are of no great value in applications, but they are useful for illustrating concepts and making crude tests of statements that are suspected of being generally true. Examples of somewhat less extreme and degenerate topological spaces abound later, when some general methods for constructing them have been developed.

Exercises

5. Find why each of the following collections is not a topology on the set Z of all integers: (a) the collection of all finite subsets of Z; (b) the collection of all infinite subsets of Z; (c) the collection of all subsets of Z whose complements (*Sets*, 16) are finite; (d) the collection of all subsets of Z of which 0 is an element; (e) the collection of all subsets of Z of which 0 is not an element.

6. On a set with two elements, say $S = \{a, b\}$, there are four topologies: $\{\emptyset, S\}$, $\{\emptyset, \{a\}, S\}$, $\{\emptyset, \{b\}, S\}$, and the discrete topology. Find the twenty-nine different topologies on a set $\{a, b, c\}$ with three distinct elements.

7. Show that if S is any nonempty set, the collection consisting of the empty set and those subsets of S whose complements (*Sets*, 16) are finite is a topology on S. This topology will be called the *cofinite* topology in later exercises. Prove that the cofinite topology is discrete if and only if S is finite.

Neighborhoods. If $(S, \Im)$ is a topological space, and $x \in S$, a subset N of S is called a *neighborhood* of x if there exists an open set U such that $x \in U$ and $U \subset N$ (or, for short, $x \in U \subset N$). In other words, N is a neighborhood of x if it is a superset of some open set to which x belongs. Notice that this concept of a neighborhood differs from those mentioned in the preceding informal discussions.

In this book, the fact that N is a neighborhood of x is indicated by writing $x \prec N$; the notation is not customary, but it helps.

This terminology and notation have the shortcoming that they make no explicit reference to the topological space, and especially to the

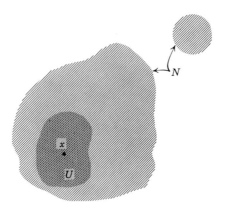

A neighborhood

topology, concerned. This ambiguity can be avoided by resorting to such notations as "𝔍-neighborhood" and "$x \prec N(𝔍)$," but in practice such fastidious attention to specifying the topology is not usually necessary. When it is important to be definite about what topology is involved, it is customary to make rather vague use of the word "in," saying for example "N is a neighborhood of x in $(S, 𝔍)$" or "$x \prec N$ in $(S, 𝔍)$." The same preposition is used similarly in company with other terms to be defined in connection with topological spaces.

SOME EXTREME EXAMPLES OF NEIGHBORHOODS. In a discrete topological space (that is, one whose topology is the discrete topology), $x \prec X$ if and only if $x \in X$; in a trivial topological space, the only neighborhood (and it is a neighborhood of every point) is the ground set. More interesting examples of neighborhoods appear shortly.

The definition of a neighborhood tells anyone who knows all about open sets how, in principle, to recognize neighborhoods; the following theorem tells anyone who knows all about neighborhoods how, in principle, to recognize open sets.

THEOREM 1. If $(S, 𝔍)$ is a topological space, a subset X of S is open if and only if $x \in X$ implies $x \prec X$; that is, if and only if X is a neighborhood of each of its elements.

Proof. If X is open, and $x \in X$, then X itself can be used as the open set U whose existence qualifies X to be a neighborhood of x; $x \in X \subset X$. On the other hand, if X is a neighborhood of every point belonging to it, then for each x belonging to X there exists an open set U_x such that $x \in U_x \subset X$. Then (*Sets*, 3, 6, 7, 12) $X = \cup\{\{x\} : x \in X\} \subset \cup\{U_x : x \in X\}$, and at the same time $\cup\{U_x : x \in X\} \subset X$. Therefore $X = \cup\{U_x : x \in X\}$. By ($O_1$), the latter set is open; so X is open.

Theorem 1 makes it possible to regard the open sets in a topological space as superneighborhoods: Every nonempty open set is a neighborhood not only of *some* point that belongs to it, but of *every* point that belongs to it. Not all neighborhoods have this property, as very simple examples show.

The most important properties of the neighborhoods in any topological space are those in the following list.

(N_1) For each x belonging to S, there exists at least one X such that $x \prec X$.
(N_2) If $x \prec X$ and $x \prec Y$, then $x \prec X \cap Y$.
(N_3) If $x \prec X$ and $X \subset Y$, then $x \prec Y$.
(N_4) If $x \prec X$, then $x \in X$.
(N_5) If $x \prec X$, there exists a set Y such that $x \prec Y$, and $u \prec X$ for all u belonging to Y.

These properties can be described very simply in less formal terms: (N_1) says that every point has at least one neighborhood; (N_2) says that the intersection of any two neighborhoods of a point is a neighborhood of that point; and so on. The more austere formulations given above will facilitate the statement and proof of Theorem 2.

Properties (N_3) and (N_4) follow at once from the definition of a neighborhood. Every point has at least one neighborhood, namely S; hence (N_1).

The set Y whose existence is claimed by (N_5) can be taken to be any open set satisfying $x \in Y \subset X$; the definition of neighborhoods and Theorem 1 guarantee that Y has the necessary properties.

Proof of (N_2). If X and Y are neighborhoods of x, then $x \in U \subset X$ and $x \in V \subset Y$, where U and V are some open sets. But then (*Sets*, 13)

$$x \in U \cap V \subset X \cap Y,$$

and since $U \cap V$ is open according to (O_2), $X \cap Y$ is a neighborhood of x.

Because of properties (N_1)–(N_4), the collection of all neighborhoods of a point in a topological space is a filter (*Sets*, 42), and is now often called the *neighborhood filter* of that point (see Exercise 9). Fundamentally, $\prec$ is a relation between points of S and subsets of S; or, in more formal language, it is a relation from S to the collection $\mathcal{P}(S)$ of all subsets of S (*Sets*, 5, 19, 20). In general, the behavior of this relation, as compared with more familiar relations, is very irregular: given one x belonging to S, there may be many subsets X of S satisfying $x \prec X$; and for a given X, there may be many, just one, or no points x for which $x \prec X$ is true. The five properties (N_1)–(N_5) are limitations on the irregularity of a neighborhood relation. Indeed, according to the following theorem, these five properties characterize neighborhood relations.

THEOREM 2. If $\prec$ is a relation from a nonempty set S to the power set $\mathcal{P}(S)$ that satisfies (N_1)–(N_5), then there exists a unique topology $\mathfrak{I}$ on S such that $\prec$ is precisely the neighborhood relation in the topological space $(S, \mathfrak{I})$.

It is easier to describe the significance of this theorem than to prove it. Along with the remarks that precede it, Theorem 2 says that there is a one-to-one correspondence between the topologies on a set S and those relations $\prec$ from S to $\mathcal{P}(S)$ that have the properties (N_1)–(N_5). Moreover, the correspondence is of such a kind that the statement "X is a neighborhood of x" in the one case is equivalent to "$x \prec X$" in the other. On this basis a topological space could be defined as an ordered pair $(S, \prec)$, where $\prec$ is a relation of the specified kind, and then a topology $\mathfrak{I}$ on S could be defined by taking $\mathfrak{I}$ to be the topology whose existence is claimed by Theorem 2; and the ultimate results would be precisely those yielded by the original definition of a topological space. In particular, $\prec$ would be the neighborhood relation. Hausdorff's definition of a topological space can be regarded as a variant of this procedure.

Proof of Theorem 2. If there is any topology $\mathfrak{I}$ such that $\prec$ is the neighborhood relation for $(S, \mathfrak{I})$, then according to Theorem 1 that topology must be

$$\mathfrak{I} = \{X \subset S \colon \text{if } x \in X, \text{ then } x \prec X\}. \qquad (1)$$

The theorem will therefore be proved if it is shown that this $\mathfrak{I}$ is a topology on S, and that $\prec$ is indeed the neighborhood relation in $(S, \mathfrak{I})$.

First, $\mathfrak{I}$ satisfies (O_1). If $\mathfrak{U} \subset \mathfrak{I}$, then either $\bigcup\mathfrak{U} = \emptyset$ or $\bigcup\mathfrak{U} \neq \emptyset$. If $\bigcup\mathfrak{U} = \emptyset$, then $\bigcup\mathfrak{U} \in \mathfrak{I}$ because $\emptyset \in \mathfrak{I}$ according to (1). If $\bigcup\mathfrak{U} \neq \emptyset$, and if x is any element of $\bigcup\mathfrak{U}$, then by the definition of union there is some set $U \in \mathfrak{U}$ to which x belongs. But then $x \prec U$ because of (1), and so $x \prec \bigcup\mathfrak{U}$ because of (N_3) and the fact (*Sets*, 14) that $U \subset \bigcup\mathfrak{U}$. In either case, therefore, $\bigcup\mathfrak{U} \in \mathfrak{I}$.

$\mathfrak{I}$ also satisfies (O_2). If $\mathfrak{U}$ is a nonempty finite subcollection of $\mathfrak{I}$, then $\bigcap\mathfrak{U} \in \mathfrak{I}$ either because it is empty, or because if $x \in \bigcap\mathfrak{U}$, then $x \in U$ for all $U \in \mathfrak{U}$, so $x \prec U$ for all $U \in \mathfrak{U}$, and therefore, because of (N_2) (see Exercise 10), $x \prec \bigcap\mathfrak{U}$; hence $\bigcap\mathfrak{U} \in \mathfrak{I}$.

$\mathfrak{I}$ satisfies (O_3) because of (N_1) and (N_3).

This shows that $(S, \mathfrak{I})$ is a topological space when $\mathfrak{I}$ is defined by (1), and the remaining problem is to show that for any point x in this space, and for any subset X of S, $x \prec X$ (where $\prec$ is still the given relation!) if and only if there is some member U of $\mathfrak{I}$ which satisfies $x \in U \subset X$.

If $x \prec X$, one may take $U = \{y : y \prec X\}$. Clearly, $x \in U$. In addition, $U \subset X$; for if $y \in U$, then $y \prec X$ by the definition of U, so $y \in X$ because of (N_4). Finally, $U \in \mathfrak{I}$. If $y \in U$, then $y \prec X$. By (N_5), there exists a set Y with the properties (i) $y \prec Y$ and (ii) $u \prec X$ for all $u \in Y$. Property (ii) gives $Y \subset U$; and then (i) and (N_3) together yield $y \prec U$. This shows that $y \prec U$ if $y \in U$; that is, $U \in \mathfrak{I}$.

On the other hand, if there is a U belonging to $\mathfrak{I}$ which satisfies $x \in U \subset X$, then $x \prec U$ by the definition of $\mathfrak{I}$, and (N_3) yields in turn $x \prec X$. This completes the proof.

There is a simple connection between the neighborhood concept and the common mathematical phrase "sufficiently close." A brief look at this connection may impart some intuitive substance to the rather bloodless abstractions that have been under discussion.

Suppose that $(S, \mathfrak{I})$ is a topological space, that $x \in S$, and that P is some condition on elements of S. It is standard practice to say "P is satisfied by all points sufficiently close to x" with the meaning: "P is satisfied at all points of some neighborhood of x." For example, if $y \neq x$, the assertion "all points sufficiently close to x are distinct from y" would be understood to mean that all points of some neighborhood of x are distinct from y; that is, there exists a neighborhood of x to which y does not belong. (This may be true or not, depending on the topological space in question.)

Now the statement "P is satisfied at all points of some neighborhood of x" can be compressed down to "$\{x : P\}$ contains some neighborhood of x." According to (N_3), however, any set that contains a neighborhood of x is itself a neighborhood of x. Thus the statement can be shortened still further to "$\{x: P\}$ is a neighborhood of x." These remarks make it possible to put the rule of interpretation that was stated in the preceding paragraph in the following form.

"*P is satisfied by all points sufficiently close to x*"
means
"$\{y: P\}$ *is a neighborhood of x*."

This is fundamentally a definition of the phrase "sufficiently close"; but from another point of view it says something about the job that neighborhoods should be doing. The usual situation is that a person defining a topological space knows in advance, more or less precisely, what is to be meant by "sufficiently close," and introduces a topology— equivalently, a neighborhood concept—that harmonizes with the pre-conceived notion of sufficient closeness in the way just described. From this standpoint, the properties (N_1)–(N_5) of neighborhoods [or the properties (O_1)–(O_3) of open sets] can be regarded as indirect descriptions of properties that any reasonable criterion for sufficient closeness should have; and the concept of a topological space can be considered as a device for the precise and efficient implementation of the idea of sufficient closeness and of the intuitive ideas that go with it.

Exercises

8. Show that in a topological space whose topology is cofinite (Exercise 7), every neighborhood is open.

9. Suppose that for a given topological space $(S, \mathfrak{I})$ it can be said that for every x belonging to S and every condition P satisfied by x, the condition P is satisfied by all points sufficiently close to x. What is $\mathfrak{I}$?

10. Show that if $\mathfrak{X}$ is a nonempty finite collection of neighborhoods of x, then $\bigcap\mathfrak{X}$ is a neighborhood of x.

11. Verify in detail that the collection of neighborhoods of a given point in a topological space is a filter (*Sets*, 42).

*12. Let Z be the set of integers, and take $x \prec X$ to mean: For some positive integer n, $\{x + k2^n: k \in Z\} \subset X$. Show that this $\prec$ has the properties (N_1)–(N_5).

*13. Construct an example of a relation $\prec$ from some nonempty set S to $\mathcal{P}(S)$ that satisfies three of the conditions (N_1)–(N_4), but not all four. In what ways, if any, does the corresponding collection $\mathfrak{I}$ defined by (1) fail to be a topology?

The Prototype: Euclidean Spaces. Many of the fundamental concepts of general topology had their beginnings in the study of n-dimensional Euclidean spaces, which in turn arose out of partly algebraic, partly geometric nineteenth-century efforts to generalize the line, plane, and "space" studied by the ancient Greek geometers, notably by Euclid in his *Elements*. These spaces continue to provide general topology with rich and important examples, and also with serious unsolved problems. The brief introduction to Euclidean spaces that follows will yield the material for illustrative examples in subsequent sections and should also make it quite clear that not all topological spaces are quaint oddities like those presented as examples earlier in this chapter.

The ground set for n-dimensional Euclidean space (where n is a positive integer) is the set of all n-tuples of real numbers, $x = (x_1, \ldots, x_n)$. In other words, it is the Cartesian product (*Sets*, 33) of n replicas of the set R of real numbers. It is therefore natural to denote this ground set by R^n, as is done in this book.

The topology on R^n can be defined in terms of the concept of an (open) n-cell. If $x \in R^n$, and α is any positive real number, the n-cell of center x and radius α is the set

$$C(x, \alpha) = \{y \in R^n : (y_1 - x_1)^2 + \cdots + (y_n - x_n)^2 < \alpha^2\}.$$

The typical 1-cell is therefore an "open interval" in R^1; that is, a set of the form

$$\{y_1 \in R^1 : x_1 - \alpha < y_1 < x_1 + \alpha\}.$$

If R^2 is identified with a plane, à la analytic geometry, the typical 2-cell can be described as the set of all points inside some circle; similarly, the typical 3-cell can be described as the set of points inside some sphere.

The following observation about n-cells will be useful soon: If $\mathcal{C}$ is any finite nonempty collection of n-cells (where n is fixed), and $x \in \cap \mathcal{C}$, there exists a positive real number α such that $C(x, \alpha) \subset \cap \mathcal{C}$. In fact, let $C(y, \beta)$ be one of the members of $\mathcal{C}$. Since $x \in C(y, \beta)$, the quantity

$$\beta - [(x_1 - y_1)^2 + \cdots + (x_n - y_n)^2]^{\frac{1}{2}}$$

is positive. If α is the smallest of these quantities as $C(y, \beta)$ ranges over $\mathcal{C}$, then if $C(y, \beta) \in \mathcal{C}$ and $u \in C(x, \alpha)$,

$$[(u_1 - y_1)^2 + \cdots + (u_n - y_n)^2]^{\frac{1}{2}}$$
$$\leq [(u_1 - x_1)^2 + \cdots + (u_n - x_n)^2]^{\frac{1}{2}}$$
$$+ [(x_1 - y_1)^2 + \cdots + (x_n - y_n)^2]^{\frac{1}{2}}$$
$$< \alpha + [(x_1 - y_1)^2 + \cdots + (x_n - y_n)^2]^{\frac{1}{2}} \leq \beta.$$

Therefore $u \in C(y, \beta)$, so $C(x, \alpha) \subset C(y, \beta)$ for all $C(y, \beta) \in \mathcal{C}$, and $C(x, \alpha) \subset \cap \mathcal{C}$. The first step in the chain of inequalities just given is based on the standard inequality

$$[(a_1 + b_1)^2 + \cdots + (a_n + b_n)^2]^{\frac{1}{2}}$$
$$\leq (a_1{}^2 + \cdots + a_n{}^2)^{\frac{1}{2}} + (b_1{}^2 + \cdots + b_n{}^2)^{\frac{1}{2}},$$

which is valid when the a_k's and b_k's are any real numbers.*

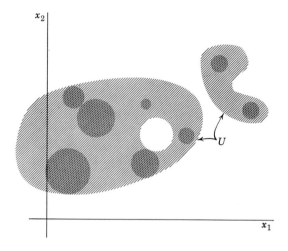

An open set in R^2

The *standard topology* $\mathfrak{I}_n$ on R^n is then defined as the collection of all subsets of R^n which are unions of collections of n-cells; that is, a subset X of R^n is open if and only if there is some collection $\mathcal{C}$ of n-cells such that $X = \cup \mathcal{C}$. In particular, every n-cell is open because it is the union of its singleton. The figure shows a typical open set U in R^2 with a few specimen 2-cells from a possible corresponding collection $\mathcal{C}$.

---

* For a proof of this inequality, see E. F. Beckenbach and R. Bellman, *Inequalities*, Springer-Verlag, Berlin, 1961, pp. 19–20.

For each n, $\mathfrak{I}_n$ really is a topology on R^n. It is easy to see that $\mathfrak{I}_n$ satisfies (O_1) and (O_3) (R^n is the union of the collection of all n-cells). $\mathfrak{I}_n$ also satisfies (O_2); if $\mathfrak{U}$ is any nonempty finite subcollection of $\mathfrak{I}_n$, and $x \in \cap\mathfrak{U}$ [if $\cap\mathfrak{U} = \emptyset$ there is nothing to prove, because $\emptyset \in \mathfrak{I}_n$ by (O_1)], then for each $U \in \mathfrak{U}$ there exists an n-cell $C(y_U, \beta_U)$ satisfying $x \in C(y_U, \beta_U) \subset U$, so

$$x \in \cap\{C(y_U, \beta_U) : U \in \mathfrak{U}\} \subset \cap\mathfrak{U}$$

(*Sets*, 13). But then, by the observation proved earlier about n-cells, there exists an n-cell $C(x, \alpha_x)$ satisfying

$$C(x, \alpha_x) \subset \cap\mathfrak{U}.$$

As in the proof of Theorem 1, it follows from this that

$$\cup\{C(x, \alpha_x) : x \in \cap\mathfrak{U}\} = \cap\mathfrak{U},$$

so $\cap\mathfrak{U} \in \mathfrak{I}_n$.

The topological space $(R^n, \mathfrak{I}_n)$ is *n-dimensional Euclidean space*, or *Euclidean n-space*. Because it is relatively seldom that any topology but the standard topology $\mathfrak{I}_n$ is assigned to R^n, it is common and moderately safe to use the symbol R^n alone as an abbreviation for $(R^n, \mathfrak{I}_n)$, and it is so used in this book. The context should always make it clear whether the symbol R^n is being used for the set of all n-tuples of real numbers or for the space $(R^n, \mathfrak{I}_n)$. The topological space R^1 is often called the *real line*, R^2 the *Euclidean plane*.

If $x \in R^n$, a neighborhood of x is any set containing a member of $\mathfrak{I}_n$ that in turn has x as an element. Because of the specific definition of open sets in R^n, a neighborhood of x can also be described as any set containing an n-cell to which x belongs. Together with Theorem 1, this provides a simple test for openness: A set is open if and only if, for every point x in the set, there exists an n-cell contained in the set that has x as an element. This may also be deduced directly from the definition of open sets.

EXAMPLES. The set $Q = \{(x, y) : x > 0 \text{ and } y > 0\}$ in R^2 is open. Let $(x_0, y_0) \in Q$. Then if α is the smaller of the two numbers x_0 and y_0, hence positive, the 2-cell

$$C = \{(x, y) : (x - x_0)^2 + (y - y_0)^2 < \alpha^2\}$$

is contained in Q and has (x_0, y_0) as an element. That $(x_0, y_0) \in C$ is easily verified. It is geometrically clear that $C \subset Q$ (see the accompanying figure), but the following kind of algebraic verification has the

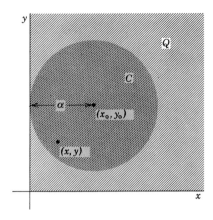

advantage that it can be extended to n-dimensional problems where very little is "geometrically clear." Suppose that $(x, y) \in C$. Then

$$(x - x_0)^2 + (y - y_0)^2 < \alpha^2.$$

It follows from this that $(x - x_0)^2 < \alpha^2$, whence $-\alpha < x - x_0$. Then $x > x_0 - \alpha \geq 0$. Thus $x > 0$, and similarly $y > 0$. This shows that $(x, y) \in Q$, as required.

On the other hand, the set $X = \{(x, y) : x > 0 \text{ and } y = 0\}$ is not open in R^2. This can be proved by showing that X contains no 2-cell whatever. If it did contain a 2-cell

$$C = \{(x, y) : (x - x_0)^2 + (y - y_0)^2 < \alpha^2\},$$

the two points (x_0, y_0) and $(x_0, y_0 + \alpha/2)$, both of which belong to C, would also belong to X; but this is impossible, because y_0 and $y_0 + \alpha/2$ cannot both be zero.

The Euclidean spaces R^n have properties that can be expressed in purely topological terms but are not shared by all topological spaces. Nevertheless, these spaces are typical enough of topological spaces in general to serve as a useful guide to thinking about many aspects of the theory. In fact, it is a good practice to make (actually or only mentally) an illustrative sketch, say for the Euclidean plane, to clarify new topological ideas as they come along. Conclusions based on these sketches, however, are only as good as the rigorous formal proofs that can be supplied for them. It should always be remembered that such sketches may mislead by showing things that, although apparently true in Euclidean spaces, or at least in the Euclidean plane, are not true in all topological spaces; and they may be inadequate for showing some of the things that may happen in Euclidean spaces themselves.

Exercises

14. Prove that X is a neighborhood of x in R^n if and only if X contains an n-cell whose *center* is x.

15. Determine whether each of the following sets in R^2 is open, and justify your conclusion in each case: (a) $\{(x, y): x < 0\}$; (b) $\{(x, y): y = 0\}$; (c) $\{(x, y): |y| < |x|\}$; (d) $\{(x, y): x^2 + y^2 < 0\}$; $(*e)$ $\{(x, y): x - y \text{ is rational}\}$.

16. The *positive orthant* in R^n is the set of all n-tuples of positive real numbers. Show that the positive orthant in any Euclidean space is open.

17. Find a nonempty collection of open sets in R^2 whose intersection is not open.

18. Of which points in R^2 is the set $\{(x, y): |x| + |y| \le 1\}$ a neighborhood?

Closed Sets. If $(S, \mathfrak{I})$ is a topological space, and X is a subset of S, then X is said to be *closed* in $(S, \mathfrak{I})$ if $S - X$ is open or, equivalently, if there exists an open set U such that $X = S - U$.

Unlike doors, sets in a given topological space may be both open and closed, or neither open nor closed. For example, in the topological space whose ground set is $S = \{a, b, c\}$ and whose topology is $\{\emptyset, \{a\}, \{b, c\}, S\}$, the set a is both open and closed, whereas the sets $\{b\}$ and $\{c\}$ are neither open nor closed. In any topological space, the empty set and the ground set are both open and both closed. In a discrete topological space, every set is both open and closed. In a trivial topological space, any nonempty set different from the ground set is neither open nor closed.

The collection $\mathcal{G}$ of closed sets in any topological space (there is no standard term for it; "cotopology" might be a good one) has three basic properties:

(G_1) The intersection of any nonempty subcollection of $\mathcal{G}$ belongs to $\mathcal{G}$.
(G_2) The union of any finite subcollection of $\mathcal{G}$ belongs to $\mathcal{G}$.
(G_3) $S \in \mathcal{G}$.

The properties (G_1) and (G_2) for nonempty subcollections of $\mathcal{G}$ can be derived directly from the properties (O_1) and (O_2) of $\mathfrak{I}$ by use of the appropriate De Morgan formulas (*Sets*, 17), and (G_2) for the empty subcollection of $\mathcal{G}$, whose union is $\emptyset$, follows at once from (O_3). Similarly, (G_3) follows from the previous remark that $\emptyset$ is always open.

The properties (G_1)–(G_3) characterize the collection of closed sets in a topological space in just the way that the properties (N_1)–(N_5) characterize neighborhood relations. This fact is expressed more precisely by:

THEOREM 3. If $\mathcal{G}$ is a collection of subsets of a nonempty set S which satisfies (G_1)–(G_3), there exists a unique topology $\mathfrak{I}$ on S such that $\mathcal{G}$ is precisely the collection of closed sets in the topological space $(S, \mathfrak{I})$.

The topology $\mathfrak{I}$ has to be the collection

$$\{X : S - X \in \mathcal{G}\}.$$

It requires more care than ingenuity, and is therefore left as an exercise, to prove that this $\mathfrak{I}$ has the necessary properties.

The procedure for showing that a set in R^n is open that was described and illustrated in the preceding section immediately yields a procedure for showing that a set in R^n is closed; for, by the definition of a closed set, showing that a set is closed is equivalent to showing that its complement is open. Thus the verification of the fact that the set

$$Q = \{(x, y) : x > 0 \text{ and } y > 0\}$$

is open in R^2 was in effect a verification of the fact that its complement

$$\{(x, y) : x \leq 0 \text{ or } y \leq 0\}$$

is closed in R^2.

Exercises

19. Which of the sets listed in Exercise 15 are closed in R^2?

20. A set in R^n of the form

$$D(x, \alpha) = \{y \in R^n : (y_1 - x_1)^2 + \cdots + (y_n - x_n)^2 \leq \alpha^2\},$$

where α is positive, is called a *closed n-cell*, or sometimes an *n-disk*. Show that every closed n-cell really is closed in R^n.

21. Write out a proof of Theorem 3.

22. Find a collection of closed sets in R^1 whose union is not closed.

23. If $(S, \mathfrak{I})$ is a topological space, a collection $\mathfrak{A}$ of subsets of S is said to be *locally finite* if every point x in S has a neighborhood N such that $\{X \in \mathfrak{A} : X \cap N \neq \emptyset\}$ is finite. Prove that the union of any locally finite collection of closed sets in $(S, \mathfrak{I})$ is closed.

Closure. If $(S, \mathfrak{I})$ is a given topological space, and $X \subset S$, the collection $\mathfrak{G}(X)$ of closed supersets of X in $(S, \mathfrak{I})$ is not empty, because S belongs to it. The intersection $\cap \mathfrak{G}(X)$, which is therefore always defined, is called the *closure* of X in $(S, \mathfrak{I})$ and is commonly denoted by $\overline{X}$.

For example, consider again a topological space $(S, \mathfrak{I})$ where S is any nonempty, but preferably infinite, set, and $\mathfrak{I}$ is the cofinite topology on S (Exercise 7). Then the closed sets in $(S, \mathfrak{I})$ are S itself and the finite subsets of S. In such a space, the closure of any finite set is the set itself; but the closure of any infinite set is S.

If X and Y are any sets in a topological space $(S, \mathfrak{I})$, the following statements hold:

(K$_1$) $\overline{X \cup Y} = \overline{X} \cup \overline{Y}$.

(K$_2$) $X \subset \overline{X}$.

(K$_3$) $\overline{\overline{X}} \subset \overline{X}$.

(K$_4$) $\overline{\emptyset} = \emptyset$.

(K$_5$) $X \in \mathfrak{G}$ if and only if $\overline{X} = X$.

(K$_6$) If $X \subset Y$, then $\overline{X} \subset \overline{Y}$.

(K$_7$) $\overline{X} \in \mathfrak{G}$.

[In (K$_3$), $\overline{\overline{X}}$ denotes the closure of the closure of X. In (K$_5$) and (K$_7$), $\mathfrak{G}$ still denotes the collection of closed sets in $(S, \mathfrak{I})$.] The statements (K$_2$), (K$_4$), (K$_6$), and (K$_7$) follow more or less directly from the definition of closure and the basic properties of closed sets. For instance, one can prove (K$_7$) by simply pointing out that $\overline{X}$, as the intersection of the nonempty collection $\mathfrak{G}(X)$ of closed sets, must be closed according to (G$_1$). Using these four statements, one can readily prove (K$_5$), (K$_3$), and (K$_1$):

Proof of (K$_5$). If X is closed, then $X \in \mathfrak{G}(X)$, so $\overline{X} = \cap \mathfrak{G}(X) \subset X$; and since $X \subset \overline{X}$ according to (K$_2$), $\overline{X} = X$. Conversely, if $\overline{X} = X$ then X is closed because $\overline{X}$ is closed (K$_7$).

Proof of (K$_3$). By (K$_7$), $\overline{X}$ is closed; so, by (K$_5$), $\overline{\overline{X}} = \overline{X}$. This surely implies $\overline{\overline{X}} \subset \overline{X}$.

Proof of (K₁). $X \subset \overline{X}$ and $Y \subset \overline{Y}$ by (K₂), so $X \cup Y \subset \overline{X} \cup \overline{Y}$. It follows from (K₇) and (G₂) that $\overline{X} \cup \overline{Y}$ is also a closed set. Thus $\overline{X} \cup \overline{Y} \in \mathcal{G}(X \cup Y)$, and

$$\overline{X \cup Y} = \cap \mathcal{G}(X \cup Y) \subset \overline{X} \cup \overline{Y}. \tag{2}$$

At the same time, from $X \subset X \cup Y$ and $Y \subset X \cup Y$ statement (K₆) gives $\overline{X} \subset \overline{X \cup Y}$ and $\overline{Y} \subset \overline{X \cup Y}$. Therefore

$$\overline{X} \cup \overline{Y} \subset \overline{X \cup Y}. \tag{3}$$

Formulas (2) and (3) together give the equation sought.

Properties (K₂) and (K₇) say that $\overline{X}$ is a closed superset of X. At the same time, however, any closed superset of X must contain $\overline{X}$—this is an immediate consequence of the definition. In this sense, $\overline{X}$ may be described as the smallest closed superset of X, and this is a good way to think of closure.

Property (K₁) is equivalent to a statement that may seem to say more:

> (K₁′) If $\mathfrak{X}$ is any nonempty finite collection of subsets of S, then
> $$\overline{\cup \mathfrak{X}} = \cup\{\overline{X} : X \in \mathfrak{X}\}.$$

(K₁′) has (K₁) as a special case, but (K₁′) also follows from (K₁). This can be shown by induction on the number of members of $\mathfrak{X}$. The equation in (K₁′) may break down when $\mathfrak{X}$ is an infinite collection. For example, if $\mathfrak{X}$ is the collection of all sets in R^1 of the form

$$X_n = \{x : 1/n < x < 1 - 1/n\},$$

where n is an integer greater than 2, then according to Exercise 25 below

$$\overline{X}_n = \{x : 1/n \le x \le 1 - 1/n\},$$

and therefore, again by Exercise 25,

$$\{x : 0 \le x \le 1\} = \overline{\cup \mathfrak{X}} \ne \cup\{\overline{X} : X \in \mathfrak{X}\} = \{x : 0 < x < 1\}.$$

Properties (K₁)–(K₄) characterize closure in topological spaces.

THEOREM 4. If S is a nonempty set, and $X \to \overline{X}$ is a function (*Sets*, 24) from $\mathcal{P}(S)$ to $\mathcal{P}(S)$ satisfying (K₁)–(K₄), then there exists a unique topology $\mathfrak{I}$ on S such that for any subset X of S, $\overline{X}$ is the closure of X in $(S, \mathfrak{I})$.

This justifies the alternative of defining a topological space as a non-empty set S with such a function $X \to \overline{X}$. Because this was in fact almost the definition given by C. Kuratowski in a paper published in 1922, (K_1)–(K_4) are often called *Kuratowski's axioms*.

The strategy of the proof of Theorem 4 is to show that once there is given a function $X \to \overline{X}$ of the specified kind, there is a unique collection $\mathcal{G}$ which could be the collection of closed sets in a space $(S, \mathfrak{I})$ for which $X \to \overline{X}$ is the closure function; that this $\mathcal{G}$ does satisfy (G_1)–(G_3) and therefore, according to Theorem 3, uniquely defines an appropriate topology $\mathfrak{I}$ on S; and that $X \to \overline{X}$ is indeed the closure function for $(S, \mathfrak{I})$.

First, in view of (K_5), the only candidate for $\mathcal{G}$ is the collection defined by

$$\mathcal{G} = \{X \subset S \colon \overline{X} = X\}.$$

Since (K_1)–(K_4) hold by assumption, and (K_5) is now true by definition, the rest of the proof may make free use of (K_1)–(K_7) on the strength of Exercise 26.

$\mathcal{G}$ *Satisfies* (G_1). If $\mathfrak{K}$ is any nonempty subcollection of $\mathcal{G}$, and $X \in \mathfrak{K}$, then $\cap \mathfrak{K} \subset X$; so, by (K_6), $\overline{\cap \mathfrak{K}} \subset \overline{X} = X$. From this it follows that $\overline{\cap \mathfrak{K}} \subset \cap \mathfrak{K}$. The opposite inclusion is assured by (K_2), so in fact $\overline{\cap \mathfrak{K}} = \cap \mathfrak{K}$; that is, $\cap \mathfrak{K} \in \mathcal{G}$.

$\mathcal{G}$ *Satisfies* (G_2). If $\mathfrak{K}$ is the empty subcollection of $\mathcal{G}$, then $\cup \mathfrak{K} = \emptyset$, and this belongs to $\mathcal{G}$ because of (K_4). If $\mathfrak{K}$ is a nonempty finite subcollection of $\mathcal{G}$, then (K_1')—which follows from (K_1)—gives

$$\overline{\cup \mathfrak{K}} = \cup\{\overline{X} \colon X \in \mathfrak{K}\} = \cup\{X \colon X \in \mathfrak{K}\} = \cup \mathfrak{K}.$$

Therefore $\cup \mathfrak{K} \in \mathcal{G}$.

$\mathcal{G}$ *Satisfies* (G_3). Because of (K_2), $S \subset \overline{S}$; and since $\overline{S}$ must be some subset of S, $\overline{S} = S$; so $S \in \mathcal{G}$.

Now it has been shown that $\mathcal{G}$ satisfies the conditions of Theorem 3, so there is a unique topological space $(S, \mathfrak{I})$ for which $\mathcal{G}$ is the collection of closed sets, and for which $X \to \overline{X}$ could be the closure function. In fact, this is the closure function in this space. If X is any subset of S, then $X \subset \overline{X}$ by (K_2), and $\overline{X} \in \mathcal{G}$ by (K_7). Since the closure of X is contained in any closed superset of X,

(closure of X) $\subset \overline{X}$.

On the other hand, if F is any closed superset of X, then $\bar{X} \subset \bar{F} = F$ by (K_6) and the definition of $\mathcal{G}$, and therefore, since the intersection of the collection of all closed supersets F is the closure of X,

$$\bar{X} \subset (\text{closure of } X).$$

The last two displays together give the needed equation

$$\bar{X} = (\text{closure of } X),$$

and the proof is complete.

Exercises

24. Let $S = \{a, b, c, d\}$ and $\mathfrak{I} = \{\emptyset, \{a\}, \{a, b\}, \{a, b, c\}, S\}$. Find the closure of each of the sixteen sets in $(S, \mathfrak{I})$.

25. If a and b are real numbers, and $a < b$, show that

$$\overline{\{x : a < x < b\}} = \{x : a \leq x \leq b\}$$

in R^1.

26. The statements (K_1)–(K_7) are highly nonindependent. Show this by deriving (K_6) and (K_7) from (K_1)–(K_5) without using any other properties of closed sets or closure.

27. Show that if $\mathfrak{X}$ is any collection of sets in a topological space, then $\overline{\cap \mathfrak{X}} \subset \cap\{\bar{X} : X \in \mathfrak{X}\}$. Find an example to show that the two sets need not be equal.

28. Let Z^+ be the set of positive integers, and for each $X \subset Z^+$ put $\bar{X} = \{x \in Z^+ : x \text{ is divisible by some element of } X\}$. Prove that this function $X \to \bar{X}$ satisfies (K_1)–(K_4). Find an interesting example of an open set in the corresponding topological space.

*29. Consider the set $S = \{a, b, c\}$, with the function $X \to \bar{X}$ defined by

$$\bar{X} = X \quad \text{if } X = \emptyset,$$
$$\bar{X} = X \cup \{a\} \quad \text{if } a \notin X \text{ but } X \neq \emptyset,$$
$$\bar{X} = X \cup \{b\} \quad \text{if } a \in X.$$

Which of Kuratowski's axioms are satisfied here? Show that $\mathfrak{I}$, as defined indirectly in the proof of Theorem 4, is a topology in this case, but that $\bar{X}$ is not always the closure of X in the topological space $(S, \mathfrak{I})$.

Topologization. As several previous remarks suggest, Theorems 2, 3, and 4 make it possible to specify a topology on a set S not only directly, by saying just which subsets of S shall be open, but also indirectly, by saying what shall be the neighborhood relation, the collection of closed sets, or the closure function. In each case, a compatible topology is uniquely determined. Any such way of directly or indirectly specifying a topology on S is called a means of *topologizing* S. Many of the topological concepts that will be defined later can be incorporated into methods of topologization in the same general way.

It is no great step to convert each of these methods of topologization into an alternative definition of the concept of a topological space itself. As was pointed out in connection with Theorem 2, for example, one might choose to define a topological space as a pair $(S, \prec)$, where S is any nonempty set and $\prec$ is a relation from S into $\mathcal{P}(S)$ which satisfies (N_1)–(N_5). This leads naturally to an appropriate definition of open sets, and in turn to definitions of closed sets, closure, and so on. As the upshot, one has essentially the same theory as if one had started with the definition given at the beginning of this chapter; and of course it is the theory that one obtains, not how it is organized, that matters most. Indeed, many of the alternative definitions of a topological space that can be formulated in this way can be found in the literature. The decision to thrust a particular concept into the leading role is based on considerations of convenience.

A somewhat different approach to the topologization problem is discussed in Chapter 4.

Adherent Points. In this section, and as a rule hereafter, the now familiar opening phrase "If $(S, \mathfrak{I})$ is a topological space" is omitted from many statements in which it might be expected to appear. Unless there are clear indications to the contrary, it should be assumed that each discussion concerns phenomena in an unspecified topological space whose ground set is denoted by S, whose topology is denoted by $\mathfrak{I}$, whose neighborhood relation is denoted by $\prec$, and so forth. The notation $\mathsf{C}X$ will regularly be used for the set $S - X$, the complement of X in S.

A point x is called an *adherent point* of a set X if $x \in \overline{X}$. Clearly, a point x can be an adherent point of a set X either by belonging to X or by belonging to $\overline{X} - X$—that is, to every closed superset of X but not to X itself.

Because of the property (K_6) of closure, if a point x is an adherent point of any subset of X, it is an adherent point of X. Thus, in particular, if x is an adherent point of $X - \{x\}$, it is an adherent point of X. A point x satisfying $x \in \overline{X - \{x\}}$ is a *cluster point* of X; any cluster point of X is therefore an adherent point of X. The set of all cluster points of a set X is called the *derived set* of X, and is conventionally denoted by X'.

Adherent points of X which are not cluster points of X are called *isolated points* of X. The set of isolated points of X is simply $X - X'$.

THEOREM 5. A point x is an adherent point of a set X if and only if every neighborhood N of x satisfies $N \cap X \neq \emptyset$.

This statement is logically equivalent to "x is not an adherent point of X ($x \notin \bar{X}$) if and only if x has a neighborhood disjoint from X." This is true: If $x \notin \bar{X}$, then the set $\mathbf{C}\bar{X}$ is a neighborhood of x disjoint from X. On the other hand, if $x \prec N$ and $N \cap X = \emptyset$, and U is an open set satisfying $x \in U \subset N$, then $\mathbf{C}U$ is a closed set containing X, and therefore containing $\bar{X}$. From $x \notin \mathbf{C}U$ it follows that $x \notin \bar{X}$.

On the basis of Theorem 5, one can immediately describe the cluster points of a set X as those points x for which $N \cap (X - \{x\}) \neq \emptyset$ for every neighborhood N of x. Similarly, an isolated point of X can be described as a point x having a neighborhood N that satisfies $N \cap X = \{x\}$. Theorem 5 and these remarks provide extremely useful criteria for finding adherent points (hence closure), cluster points, and isolated points in specific instances.

EXAMPLES. Consider again the set

$$Q = \{(x, y): x > 0 \text{ and } y > 0\}$$

in R^2. By methods similar to those used in the first example on p. 21, it can be shown that every 2-cell centered at (x_0, y_0) has a nonempty intersection with Q if and only if $x_0 \geq 0$ and $y_0 \geq 0$. From this it follows, by Theorem 5 and Exercise 14, that the set of all adherent points (that is, the closure) of Q is

$$\{(x, y): x \geq 0 \text{ and } y \geq 0\}.$$

Moreover, since the intersection of such a 2-cell with Q is never just $\{(x_0, y_0)\}$, every adherent point is a cluster point. Q has no isolated points.

Now let $X = \{(1 + 2^{-m}, 1 + 2^{-n}): m, n = 0, 1, 2, \ldots\}$. This set is shown in the accompanying figure, from which it may or may not be clear that the following statements are correct: (i) Every point of X is isolated. (ii) The one and only cluster point of X is $(1, 1)$.

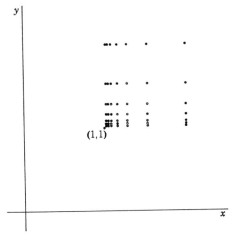

A cluster point in R^2

Proof of (i). Let $x_{mn} = (1 + 2^{-m}, 1 + 2^{-n})$ be any point of X. Then the 2-cell C_{mn} whose center is x_{mn} and whose radius is 2^{-m-n-1} is a neighborhood of x_{mn} that satisfies $C_{mn} \cap X = \{x_{mn}\}$, as required. The verification of this statement is a matter of elementary but somewhat lengthy calculation and is omitted.

Proof of (ii). Since every point of X is isolated, any cluster point of X must belong to CX. The point $(1, 1)$ is indeed a cluster point of X. If C is a 2-cell centered at this point whose radius is α, then $(1 + 2^{-p}, 1 + 2^{-p}) \in C \cap X$ if p is any non-negative integer that satisfies $p > \frac{1}{2} - \log_2 \alpha$. From this it follows, by Exercise 14 again, that any neighborhood N of $(1, 1)$ satisfies $N \cap X \neq \emptyset$, and since $(1, 1) \notin X$, this makes $(1, 1)$ a cluster point of X. The remaining step, that of showing that no other point of CX is a cluster point of X, is cumbersome but not really difficult and is omitted.

A notion of closeness may again be introduced here to bring some specific intuitive content to these general concepts. When a mathematician says that a condition P is satisfied at points "arbitrarily close" to a point x, he normally means that no matter what standard of closeness to x is specified—that is, no matter what may be meant by "sufficiently close" to x—there are points that meet this standard and satisfy P. In view of the discussion of sufficient closeness, it is natural to take this in turn to mean that to every neighborhood of x

there belongs at least one point that satisfies P: If $x \not\prec N$, then $N \cap \{y\!:\!P\} \neq \emptyset$. Theorem 5 may be used to simplify this still further, and the result is the following rule of interpretation.

"*P is satisfied by points arbitrarily close to x*"

means

"$x \in \overline{\{y\!:\!P\}}$."

Consider, for example, the case where P is the condition $y \in X$, X being some fixed set. In this case $x \in \overline{\{y\!:\!P\}}$ becomes $x \in \overline{X}$, so by the rule, "$y \in X$ for points y arbitrarily close to x" means "$x \in \overline{X}$." In other words, the closure of a set X consists of all points x such that there are points of X arbitrarily close to x. Similarly, an adherent point of X is a point that has points of X arbitrarily close to it; a cluster point of X is a point x that has points of $X - \{x\}$ arbitrarily close to it; and an isolated point is a point x of X that does *not* have points of $X - \{x\}$ arbitrarily close to it. These statements may be regarded as expressions of the intended intuitive significance of the terms closure, adherent point, and so on. The very terms themselves tend to reflect this significance.

Exercises

30. Describe the derived set of each of the following sets in R^1: (a) $\{1\}$; (b) $\{x\!:\!0 < x < 1\}$; (c) $\{x\!:\!x^{-1}$ is an integer$\}$; (d) $\{x\!:\!x$ is rational$\}$.

31. In an infinite set with the cofinite topology (Exercise 7) which sets have cluster points?

32. A set X that satisfies $X = X'$ is said to be *perfect*. Prove that a set is perfect if and only if it is closed and has no isolated points.

33. Some topological spaces have the property that for any point x and any set X, if there are points of X arbitrarily close to x then all points sufficiently close to x belong to X. Describe this property as simply as possible in the technical terminology that has been introduced, and find an example of a topological space that has it.

34. Show that Theorem 5 remains true if "open" is inserted before "neighborhood."

Other Operations in Topological Spaces. There are other significant operations on sets in topological spaces besides closure and "derivation," the operation that leads from a set to its derived set.

The three defined below are encountered especially often. Each of them can be defined in a variety of ways; the definitions given here have the advantage that they relate directly to the topology. Some of the equivalent definitions that appear implicitly in the exercises may be easier to use in the actual application of these operations to specific sets.

The *interior* of a set X is the union of the collection of all open subsets of X, and is denoted by X°. It follows from (O_1) that X° is always open. Indeed, just as $\overline{X}$ is the smallest closed superset of X, the set X° is the largest open subset of X. A point x is called an *interior point* of X if $x \in X^\circ$.

The *exterior* of a set X is the interior of $\mathbf{C}X$. In this section, the exterior of X is denoted by the nonstandard symbol $e(X)$. A point x is an *exterior point* of X if $x \in e(X)$.

The *boundary* of a set X is $\mathbf{C}(X^\circ \cup e(X))$. Thus a point x belongs to the boundary of X (and is therefore called a *boundary point* of X) if and only if it is neither an interior point nor an exterior point of X. In the exercises the boundary of X is denoted by $b(X)$.

EXAMPLE. Let $X = \{x \in R^1 : 0 \le x < 1 \text{ or } x = 2\}$. According to the definition of open sets in R^1, the union of the collection of all open subsets of X can also be described as the union of the collection of all 1-cells contained in X. This union is easily shown to be $\{x \in R^1 : 0 < x < 1\}$. Thus

$$X^\circ = \{x \in R^1 : 0 < x < 1\}.$$

Similarly,

$$e(X) = \{x \in R^1 : x < 0, 1 < x < 2, \text{ or } 2 < x\}.$$

For the boundary of X this leaves the set $\{0, 1, 2\}$. These results show how the interior, exterior, and boundary of a set in a Euclidean space tend to be just what the common meaning of the words might lead anyone to expect.

Two further terms should be introduced in this chapter, although they do not represent operations on sets. A set X is *dense in* the set Y if $Y \subset \overline{X}$. When X is dense in S, the ground set, it is simply said to be *dense;* "everywhere dense" is a frequently met synonym for "dense." For example, the set X of rational numbers is dense in R^1: Any 1-cell, and therefore any neighborhood of any point of R^1, has rational elements, so according to Theorem 5 every point of R^1 is an adherent point of X, and this amounts to saying that X is dense.

Similarly, if S is an infinite set with the cofinite topology (Exercise 7), any infinite subset of S is dense.

A set X is *nowhere dense* if the interior of the closure of X is empty. For example, any finite set in R^n is nowhere dense because if X is finite, $\overline{X} = X$, and the only open subset of a finite set in such a space is $\emptyset$.

A formidable number of terms have been introduced in this chapter, and by now it should come as no surprise that each of the concepts represented by these terms not only has properties of its own, but also is bound to the others by various general relationships. Exercises 41–57 form a list of such properties and relationships; they are in effect small theorems, and the problem is to prove them. This list is by no means exhaustive, and there is much to be learned from trying to lengthen it. In these exercises X and Y stand for any sets, and x stands for any point, in a given topological space.

Exercises

35. Find the interior, exterior, and boundary of each of the sets listed in Exercise 30.

36. Find the interior, exterior, and boundary of each of the sets listed in Exercise 15.

37. Which of the sets listed in Exercise 15 are dense in R^2? Which are nowhere dense?

38. Show that in a topological space whose topology is trivial, the interior of any set but S is empty; the exterior of any set but $\emptyset$ is empty; the boundary of any set is empty; any nonempty set is dense; $\emptyset$ is the only nowhere dense set.

39. Find and prove the statements corresponding to those in Exercise 38 for the case in which the topology is discrete.

40. Formulate definitions of the following concepts in terms of sufficient and arbitrary closeness: Interior point of X; exterior point of X; boundary point of X; dense. It may help to use some of the subsequent exercises.

41. If $X \subset Y$, then $X' \subset Y'$.

42. $(X \cup Y)' = X' \cup Y'$.

43. $\overline{X} = X \cup X'$.

44. If $X \subset Y$, then $e(Y) \subset e(X)$.

45. $x \prec X$ if and only if $x \in X^\circ$.

46. $\{\overline{X}, e(X)\}$ is a partition of S (*Sets*, 36).

47. $b(X) = \overline{X} \cap (\overline{\mathsf{C}X})$.

48. $b(X) = \overline{X} - X^\circ$.

49. X is open if and only if $X \cap b(X) = \emptyset$.

50. $\overline{X} = X \cup b(X)$.

51. $X^\circ = X - b(X)$.

52. $\mathsf{C}(X^\circ) = \overline{\mathsf{C}X}$.

53. The only closed dense set is S.

54. If X is dense and open, $\mathsf{C}X$ is nowhere dense.

55. No dense set is nowhere dense.

56. X is nowhere dense if and only if every nonempty open set contains a nonempty open set that is disjoint from X.

57. If X is open, $X \cap \overline{Y} \subset \overline{X \cap Y}$.

*58. Find a list of properties of the interior operation analogous to the properties (K_1)–(K_7) of the closure operation, and then formulate and prove a theorem that does for interior what Theorem 4 does for closure.

CHAPTER THREE
continuity and homeomorphism

Continuous Functions. If $(S_1, \mathfrak{I}_1)$ and $(S_2, \mathfrak{I}_2)$ are topological spaces, f is a function from S_1 into S_2, and $x \in S_1$, then the continuity of f at x can be defined just as in Chapter 1: f is *continuous at* x if, for any neighborhood N of $f(x)$ in $(S_2, \mathfrak{I}_2)$, there exists a neighborhood M of x in $(S_1, \mathfrak{I}_1)$ that satisfies $f(M) \subset N$. The fact that any superset of a neighborhood is also a neighborhood makes it possible to restate this definition in the form "f is continuous at x if $f^{-1}(N)$ is a neighborhood of x whenever N is a neighborhood of $f(x)$" (*Sets*, 20, 22). In all discussions of continuity it is important to remember that whether a function is continuous at a point depends on both of the topologies concerned. This is occasionally underscored by using some such term as "$(\mathfrak{I}_1, \mathfrak{I}_2)$-continuous" in place of "continuous," but the identity of $\mathfrak{I}_1$ and $\mathfrak{I}_2$ is usually clear from the context.

If f is continuous at every point x belonging to S_1, one simply says that f is *continuous*. Continuous functions may be characterized more directly, as in Theorem 6.

THEOREM 6. If $(S_1, \mathfrak{I}_1)$ and $(S_2, \mathfrak{I}_2)$ are topological spaces, and $f\colon S_1 \to S_2$, then f is continuous if and only if, for every $V \in \mathfrak{I}_2$, $f^{-1}(V) \in \mathfrak{I}_1$.

Briefly, a continuous function is one under which the inverse image of every open set is open.

Proof. If f is continuous and $V \in \mathfrak{I}_2$, then $f^{-1}(V) \in \mathfrak{I}_1$: If $f^{-1}(V) = \emptyset$, there is nothing to prove, because necessarily $\emptyset \in \mathfrak{I}_1$. If $x \in f^{-1}(V) \neq \emptyset$, then, since V is a neighborhood of $f(x)$ (Theorem

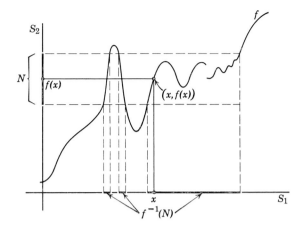

Continuity at x

1), $f^{-1}(V)$ is a neighborhood of x according to the assumption that f is continuous; and as a neighborhood of each of its points, $f^{-1}(V)$ is open. Conversely, if $f^{-1}(V) \in \mathfrak{I}_1$ whenever $V \in \mathfrak{I}_2$, and $f(x) \prec N$, then there exists a set $W \in \mathfrak{I}_2$ satisfying $f(x) \in W \subset N$, and therefore $x \in f^{-1}(W) \subset f^{-1}(N)$. Since $f^{-1}(W) \in \mathfrak{I}_1$, $f^{-1}(N)$ is a neighborhood of x.

Because of its simplicity, and because it is expressed directly in terms of the topologies, the characterization of continuous functions given by Theorem 6 is often taken as the definition of continuity. It follows easily from Theorem 6 that if $(S_1, \mathfrak{I}_1)$ and $(S_2, \mathfrak{I}_2)$ are topological spaces, and a function f from S_1 into S_2 is $(\mathfrak{I}_1, \mathfrak{I}_2)$-continuous, then it is also $(\mathfrak{I}_1', \mathfrak{I}_2')$-continuous if $\mathfrak{I}_1'$ is a topology on S_1 finer than $\mathfrak{I}_1$, and $\mathfrak{I}_2'$ is a topology on S_2 coarser than $\mathfrak{I}_2$. Roughly speaking, the finer the topology on S_1 and the coarser the topology on S_2, the easier it is for a given function from S_1 into S_2 to be continuous. At the extremes, if $(S_1, \mathfrak{I}_1)$ is discrete or $(S_2, \mathfrak{I}_2)$ is trivial, any function from S_1 into S_2 is continuous.

There are simple criteria for continuity based on topological concepts other than open sets and neighborhoods. Some of these criteria are given in the next theorem.

THEOREM 7. If $(S_1, \mathfrak{I}_1)$ and $(S_2, \mathfrak{I}_2)$ are topological spaces, and $f : S_1 \to S_2$, then each of the following statements implies the others:

(i) f is continuous.

(ii) If G is closed in $(S_2, \mathfrak{I}_2)$, then $f^{-1}(G)$ is closed in $(S_1, \mathfrak{I}_1)$.

(iii) For every subset X of S_1,

$$f(\overline{X}) \subset \overline{f(X)}.$$

Proof. According to Theorem 6, (i) may be replaced by "For any member V of $\mathfrak{I}_2$, $f^{-1}(V) \in \mathfrak{I}_1$." This statement in turn can be shown equivalent to (ii) by a simple manipulation of complements (*Sets*, 28); the details are omitted. (ii) implies (iii): If $X \subset S_1$, then $f(X) \subset \overline{f(X)}$ by the property (K$_2$) of closure; therefore

$$X \subset f^{-1}[f(X)] \subset f^{-1}[\overline{f(X)}].$$

The set $\overline{f(X)}$ is closed, so if (ii) is true, $f^{-1}[\overline{f(X)}]$ is a closed superset of X, and therefore of $\overline{X}$. Hence $f(\overline{X}) \subset \overline{f(X)}$, as needed. (iii) implies (ii): If G is any closed set in $(S_2, \mathfrak{I}_2)$, and (iii) is true, then

$$f[\overline{f^{-1}(G)}] \subset \overline{f[f^{-1}(G)]} \subset \overline{G} = G$$

(*Sets*, 28) and therefore $\overline{f^{-1}(G)} \subset f^{-1}(G)$. Since the opposite inclusion holds in any case, the two sets are equal, and from this it follows that $f^{-1}(G)$ is closed.

Any of these alternative characterizations of continuity can be translated into the language of sufficient and arbitrary closeness, and some of the resulting paraphrases are not bad as easily remembered informal descriptions of the concept. Thus part (iii) of Theorem 7 becomes "For any point x and set X in S_1, if there are points of X arbitrarily close to x, then there are points of $f(X)$ arbitrarily close to $f(x)$." The same idea can be expressed more concisely by saying that *continuous functions are those that preserve arbitrary closeness.* Here the word "preserve" is used in a way that is customary in topology. In general, to say that a function preserves a property or relationship is just to say that whenever any objects in the domain of the function have the property or satisfy the relationship, the same is true of the images (under the function) of those objects.

EXAMPLE. Let $f: R^1 \to R^1$ be the function defined by $f(x) = 1$ if $x \neq 0$ and $f(0) = 0$. There are points of $X = R^1 - \{0\}$ arbitrarily close to 0, but there are not points of $f(X)$, which is $\{1\}$, arbitrarily close to $f(0)$; hence f is not continuous. Naturally, the noncontinuity of this function can also be verified by use of any of the other criteria for continuity; see Exercise 59.

THEOREM 8. If $(S_1, \mathfrak{I}_1)$, $(S_2, \mathfrak{I}_2)$, and $(S_3, \mathfrak{I}_3)$ are topological spaces, $f_1 \colon S_1 \to S_2, f_2 \colon S_2 \to S_3$, and both of these functions are continuous, then the composite function $f_2 f_1 \colon S_1 \to S_3$ (*Sets*, 21, 26) is continuous.

A short proof for this theorem can be built on any of the criteria for continuity that have already been mentioned; for example, if X is any subset of S_1, then

$$f_2 f_1(\overline{X}) = f_2[f_1(\overline{X})] \subset f_2[\overline{f_1(X)}] \subset \overline{f_2[f_1(X)]} = \overline{f_2 f_1(X)},$$

by the definition of composite functions and by condition (iii) of Theorem 7 used twice. By the same condition, then, $f_2 f_1$ is continuous.

Exercises

59. Let f be the function defined in the example preceding Theorem 8. Show that f is not continuous by finding (*a*) a point x and a neighborhood N of $f(x)$ such that $f^{-1}(N)$ is not a neighborhood of x; (*b*) an open set U such that $f^{-1}(U)$ is not open; (*c*) a closed set G such that $f^{-1}(G)$ is not closed.

60. Show that, irrespective of the topologies concerned, any constant function is continuous. (A function f is constant if $f(x) = f(y)$ for all elements x and y of the domain of f.)

61. If $S = \{a, b, c\}$ and $\mathfrak{I} = \{\emptyset, \{a\}, \{a, b\}, S\}$, and f is a $(\mathfrak{I}, \mathfrak{I})$-continuous function from S into S such that $f(b) = a$ and $f(c) = b$, what is $f(a)$?

62. Let $(S, \mathfrak{I})$ be a topological space such that *every* function $f \colon S \to R^1$ is continuous. Show that $\mathfrak{I}$ must be discrete.

63. Taking S to be the set of positive integers and $\mathfrak{I}$ to be the cofinite topology on S, find a function from S *onto* S that is not $(\mathfrak{I}, \mathfrak{I})$-continuous.

64. According to one traditional definition, a function $f \colon R^2 \to R^1$ is continuous at (x_0, y_0) if, for every $\epsilon > 0$, there exists a $\delta > 0$ such that $|f(x, y) - f(x_0, y_0)| < \epsilon$ whenever $|x - x_0| < \delta$ and $|y - y_0| < \delta$. Show that this definition is equivalent to the definition at the beginning of this section when $(S_1, \mathfrak{I}_1)$ is R^2 and $(S_2, \mathfrak{I}_2)$ is R^1.

65. Formulate a criterion for continuity similar to part (iii) of Theorem 7, but based on the concept of derived set; then justify it.

Homeomorphisms. Again, suppose that $(S_1, \mathfrak{I}_1)$ and $(S_2, \mathfrak{I}_2)$ are topological spaces, and that $f \colon S_1 \to S_2$. If f is one-to-one and onto, its inverse is a function $f^{-1} \colon S_2 \to S_1$ (*Sets*, 29), and one can ask not only whether f is continuous, but also whether f^{-1} is. If both are, f is called a *homeomorphism*, or a *topological transformation*, from $(S_1, \mathfrak{I}_1)$ onto $(S_2, \mathfrak{I}_2)$. One topological space is said to be *homeomorphic* to another if there exists a homeomorphism from the first onto the second.

Because $(f^{-1})^{-1} = f$ and because of Theorem 6, a homeomorphism can also be described as a one-to-one correspondence between S_1 and S_2 with the property that for any subset X of S_1, the set $f(X) \in \mathfrak{I}_2$ if and only if $X \in \mathfrak{I}_1$. This means that a homeomorphism, which as a one-to-one correspondence neatly matches the points and sets of one space with those of the other, likewise matches the open sets of the two spaces. The matching occurs in such a way, furthermore, that subsets are matched with subsets, unions with unions, complements with complements, and so on. From this it follows that all the relationships and properties that can be formulated in terms of set theory and open sets are preserved by homeomorphisms.

TWO EXAMPLES. Let $(S_1, \mathfrak{I}_1)$ and $(S_2, \mathfrak{I}_2)$ be topological spaces, and let f be a homeomorphism from S_1 to S_2. If x is an isolated point of X in $(S_1, \mathfrak{I}_1)$, then $f(x)$ is an isolated point of $f(X)$ in $(S_2, \mathfrak{I}_2)$. In fact, let N be a neighborhood of x such that $N \cap X = \{x\}$. Then, because f is a one-to-one correspondence, $f(N) \cap f(X) = \{f(x)\}$; and because f is a homeomorphism (specifically, because f^{-1} is continuous), $f(N)$ is a neighborhood of $f(x)$; hence $f(x)$ is an isolated point of $f(X)$. $(S_1, \mathfrak{I}_1)$ is said to be *disconnected* if there exist two members U and V of $\mathfrak{I}_1$ satisfying $U \neq \emptyset$, $V \neq \emptyset$, $U \cap V = \emptyset$, and $U \cup V = S_1$. This property, which is considered at greater length in Chapter 5, is defined in terms of set theory and open sets, and should therefore be preserved by a homeomorphism; and it is. If U and V are sets in $(S_1, \mathfrak{I}_1)$ with the properties just enumerated, so that $(S_1, \mathfrak{I}_1)$ is disconnected, then the sets $f(U)$ and $f(V)$ have precisely the same properties in $(S_2, \mathfrak{I}_2)$, so this space is also disconnected. These two examples are entirely typical.

In general, a property of topological spaces that is preserved by homeomorphisms is called a *topological property*. According to the preceding remarks, topological properties include those that can be formulated in terms of set theory and open sets. A complete proof of this statement would require a very careful definition of the phrase "can be formulated in terms of set theory and open sets," and no such proof can be given here.

From an extremely puristic point of view, the general topologist as such is interested only in topological properties, and would therefore regard any two homeomorphic spaces as being essentially the same; he could make an essential distinction between two topological spaces only by noting that one had a topological property that the other lacked, and if they were homeomorphic this would be impossible. In practice, of course, topologists are also interested in nontopological properties of topological spaces.

It is valid to classify topological spaces on the basis of their being homeomorphic or not, because the relation (on any given collection of topological spaces) of being homeomorphic is an equivalence relation; it is reflexive [use the identity map (*Sets*, 25)], symmetric (use the inverse), and transitive (use Theorem 8). Accordingly (*Sets*, 34–37), the relation of being homeomorphic partitions any given collection of topological spaces into subcollections (equivalence classes), where two spaces belong to the same subcollection if and only if they are homeomorphic. These equivalence classes are sometimes called *topological types*.

There is one small point of terminology that deserves brief comment. The original definition of "homeomorphic" was unsymmetrical; it spoke of one topological space being homeomorphic to another. It later appeared, however, that this relationship is indeed symmetric. If one topological space is homeomorphic to another, then the second is also homeomorphic to the first. It is therefore not only simpler but legitimate to ignore the initial lack of symmetry and say that the two topological spaces are homeomorphic (to each other). This language has already crept into the last three paragraphs.

Exercises. The statements in Exercises 66, 67, and 68 are to be proved in detail on the assumption that f is a homeomorphism from some topological space $(S, \mathfrak{I})$ onto another, x is any element of S, and X and Y are any subsets of S.

66. The point x is a cluster point of X if and only if $f(x)$ is a cluster point of $f(X)$.

67. Y is the closure of X if and only if $f(Y)$ is the closure of $f(X)$.

68. Y is the boundary of X if and only if $f(Y)$ is the boundary of $f(X)$.

69. Let f be a homeomorphism from $(S_1, \mathfrak{I}_1)$ onto $(S_2, \mathfrak{I}_2)$, and let $(S_3, \mathfrak{I}_3)$ be some topological space. Show that a function $g: S_2 \to S_3$ is continuous if and only if $gf: S_1 \to S_3$ is continuous.

Examples of Homeomorphisms. Because of the fundamental importance of homeomorphisms and the concept of homeomorphic spaces, there is value in pausing to consider some specific examples that illustrate them. The examples discussed here, although uneven in importance, should give a general idea of how it can be shown that two spaces are, or in some cases are not, homeomorphic.

EXAMPLE 1. Let $(S_1, \mathfrak{I}_1)$ and $(S_2, \mathfrak{I}_2)$ be any two topological spaces such that there exists a one-to-one correspondence between S_1 and S_2, say f, and both $\mathfrak{I}_1$ and $\mathfrak{I}_2$ are discrete. Since $\mathfrak{I}_1$ is discrete, f must be continuous; and since $\mathfrak{I}_2$ is discrete, f^{-1} is continuous. Thus f is automatically a homeomorphism, and the two spaces are homeomorphic. If, on the other hand, there exists no one-to-one correspondence between S_1 and S_2, then *a fortiori* there can be no homeomorphism between the two spaces. Therefore *two discrete topological spaces are homeomorphic if and only if there exists a one-to-one correspondence between their ground sets.*

EXAMPLE 2. Let $S_1 = S_2 = \{a, b, c\}$, $\mathfrak{I}_1 = \{\emptyset, \{a\}, \{a, b\}, S_1\}$, and $\mathfrak{I}_2 = \{\emptyset, \{c\}, \{b, c\}, S_2\}$. Because $\mathfrak{I}_1$ and $\mathfrak{I}_2$ exhibit the same pattern, it is natural to look for a permutation (*Sets*, 29) of $\{a, b, c\}$ that matches the elements of $\mathfrak{I}_1$ with those of $\mathfrak{I}_2$. In fact, the only possible such permutation is defined by $f(a) = c$, $f(b) = b$, $f(c) = a$. It is easy to verify that with this f, the image under f of every element of $\mathfrak{I}_1$ is an element of $\mathfrak{I}_2$, and the image under f^{-1} of every element of $\mathfrak{I}_2$ is an element of $\mathfrak{I}_1$, so that f is a homeomorphism by Theorem 6, and the spaces $(S_1, \mathfrak{I}_1)$ and $(S_2, \mathfrak{I}_2)$ are homeomorphic.

EXAMPLE 3. Let S_1, S_2, and $\mathfrak{I}_1$ be as in Example 2, and let $\mathfrak{I}_2 = \{\emptyset, \{a\}, S_2\}$. The two topological spaces $(S_1, \mathfrak{I}_1)$ and $(S_2, \mathfrak{I}_2)$ are not homeomorphic. The plodding way to establish this statement would be to list all six permutations of $\{a, b, c\}$ and then to show that for one reason or another each of them fails to be a homeomorphism. A short cut is to recall that if the spaces were homeomorphic there would need to exist a one-to-one correspondence between their topologies, and then to notice that this is impossible because $\mathfrak{I}_1$ has four elements and $\mathfrak{I}_2$ has only three.

EXAMPLE 4. Take S_1 to be the 1-cell of radius 1 and center 0 in R^1, and define a topology $\mathfrak{I}_1$ on S_1 by saying that a subset X of S_1 belongs to $\mathfrak{I}_1$ if and only if X is the union of some collection of 1-cells; the method of topologization is exactly the same as that used for R^1 itself. The topological space $(S_1, \mathfrak{I}_1)$ is homeomorphic to the Euclidean line R^1. The unimpeachable way to defend this statement is to produce at least one explicit homeomorphism between the two spaces. One such homeomorphism—there are infinitely many—is the function

$f \colon S_1 \to R^1$ defined by $f(x) = x/(1 - |x|)$. It must be shown that this function is one-to-one, onto, and continuous, and that its inverse is also continuous. These problems reduce to elementary algebra, and are left as an exercise (Exercise 72). There are serious differences between the two spaces, but from the strictly topological point of view the two spaces must be considered to be essentially the same because they are homeomorphic. In fact, it is customary to call any topological space homeomorphic to either one of these spaces, and therefore to both, a 1-cell; and an analogous remark holds for n-cells in general.

EXAMPLE 5. Let S_1 and S_2 both be Z, the set of integers. Let $\mathfrak{I}_1$ be the cofinite topology (Exercise 7) on Z, and let $\mathfrak{I}_2$ be the topology on Z defined (by way of neighborhoods) in Exercise 12. The spaces $(S_1, \mathfrak{I}_1)$ and $(S_2, \mathfrak{I}_2)$ are not homeomorphic. There is no hope here, as there was in Example 3, of listing the permutations of Z and showing that there are no homeomorphisms among them. A more promising avenue of attack is to try to find a topological property that one space has and the other does not. One such property is disconnectedness (see the second example in the preceding section for the definition of this term). Indeed, if U and V are members of $\mathfrak{I}_1$, then $U \cap V = \emptyset$ only if at least one of the two sets is empty, so $(S_1, \mathfrak{I}_1)$ is not disconnected. However, if U and V are the sets of even and odd integers respectively, then both belong to $\mathfrak{I}_2$, neither is empty, their intersection is empty, and their union is S_2. Thus $(S_2, \mathfrak{I}_2)$ is disconnected. Since one of a pair of homeomorphic spaces is disconnected if and only if the other is, the spaces $(S_1, \mathfrak{I}_1)$ and $(S_2, \mathfrak{I}_2)$ cannot be homeomorphic.

Other examples of homeomorphic and nonhomeomorphic pairs of topological spaces are pointed out from time to time in subsequent chapters.

Exercises

70. Show that two trivial topological spaces are homeomorphic if and only if there exists a one-to-one correspondence between their ground sets.

71. Group the twenty-nine topological spaces with the ground set $\{a, b, c\}$ (Exercise 6) into equivalence classes determined by the relation of being homeomorphic—that is, into topological types.

72. Carry out a detailed verification of the claims made for the function f in Example 4.

73. Find a homeomorphism from the topological space $(S_1, \mathfrak{I}_1)$ of Example 4 onto R^1 that is different from the homeomorphism f.

CHAPTER FOUR

the construction of topologies

Chapter 1 had something to say about how the idea of a topological space arose, and Chapter 2 introduced some basic concepts for topological spaces and showed how some of these could be used to organize the theory in equivalent but formally different ways. This leaves the natural but still unanswered question: How does one actually go about specifying a definite topology on a given set?

Which topology should be assigned to a set, and whether it should be assigned directly or by one of the indirect routes, depend on the circumstances. In the abstract, there is no "proper," "correct," or "natural" topology to assign to a set, and no "proper," "correct," or "natural" way to assign it, any more than there is a "proper," "correct," or "natural" way to arrange paints on a given canvas in creating a painting. These epithets can have meaning only relative to some ulterior mathematical or even nonmathematical goal. Nevertheless, certain patterns of topologization occur so often that they are worth describing in detail. This chapter describes some of the more important and accessible ones.

Sub-bases. This is one common situation: A set S, and some collection α of subsets of S, are given; and for some reason one wants to define a topology on S which contains α and is no finer than it needs to be to do so. In other words, one looks for the most economical way of topologizing S so that all sets belonging to α are open in the resulting topological space.

There is always a topology meeting these specifications. In fact, let **T** be the collection of all topologies on S that contain α. This collection is not empty, because the discrete topology on S belongs to it. It is therefore legitimate to speak of the intersection $\cap \mathbf{T}$. This is a topology on S (indeed, the intersection of any nonempty collection of topologies on a set S is a topology on S); and it contains $\mathfrak{a}$. Moreover, it is the coarsest topology on S that contains $\mathfrak{a}$, just as the closure of a set X in a topological space is the smallest closed superset of X, and for exactly analogous reasons. The collection $\cap \mathbf{T}$ therefore meets the requirements set out in the preceding paragraph. It is called the *topology generated by* $\mathfrak{a}$, and will be denoted here by $\mathfrak{I}(\mathfrak{a})$. The characteristic property of $\mathfrak{I}(\mathfrak{a})$ is that it is a topology containing $\mathfrak{a}$, and if $\mathfrak{I}$ is any topology containing $\mathfrak{a}$, then $\mathfrak{I}(\mathfrak{a}) \subset \mathfrak{I}$.

Any collection of sets that generates a topology $\mathfrak{I}$ is called a *sub-base* of $\mathfrak{I}$; thus $\mathfrak{a}$ is a sub-base for $\mathfrak{I}$ if and only if $\mathfrak{I}(\mathfrak{a}) = \mathfrak{I}$.

The definition of $\mathfrak{I}(\mathfrak{a})$ is not very convenient as a means of actually finding $\mathfrak{I}(\mathfrak{a})$, given $\mathfrak{a}$. If one were to attempt to use it directly, he would need to find all the topologies on S that contain $\mathfrak{a}$ and then find their intersection; and this is no light task in any but the simplest cases. A more nearly constructive approach suggests itself. It may as well be assumed that $S \in \mathfrak{a}$, since $\mathfrak{I}(\mathfrak{a})$ must have S as a member in any case. This assumption will hold throughout the following discussion. Condition (O_2) on topologies implies that the intersection of any nonempty finite subcollection of $\mathfrak{a}$ must belong to $\mathfrak{I}(\mathfrak{a})$. If $\mathfrak{a}'$ is the collection of all such intersections, then $\mathfrak{a}' \subset \mathfrak{I}(\mathfrak{a})$. At the same time, $\mathfrak{a} \subset \mathfrak{a}'$ because if $X \in \mathfrak{a}$, then $X = \cap \{X\} \in \mathfrak{a}'$.

Then, similarly, the union of any subcollection of $\mathfrak{a}'$, as the union of a subcollection of $\mathfrak{I}(\mathfrak{a})$, must belong to $\mathfrak{I}(\mathfrak{a})$ because of (O_1). If $\mathfrak{a}''$ is the collection of all such unions, $\mathfrak{a}' \subset \mathfrak{a}'' \subset \mathfrak{I}(\mathfrak{a})$.

One might go on in this way to construct a collection $\mathfrak{a}'''$ consisting of all intersections of nonempty finite subcollections of $\mathfrak{a}''$, then a collection $\mathfrak{a}''''$ consisting of all unions of subcollections of $\mathfrak{a}'''$, and so on, using (O_1) and (O_2) in alternation, in the hope that the resulting chain of collections

$$\mathfrak{a} \subset \mathfrak{a}' \subset \mathfrak{a}'' \subset \mathfrak{a}''' \subset \cdots \; [\subset \mathfrak{I}(\mathfrak{a})]$$

would in some sense eventually exhaust $\mathfrak{I}(\mathfrak{a})$. In fact, the exhaustion sets in early:

THEOREM 9. $\qquad\qquad \mathfrak{a}'' = \mathfrak{I}(\mathfrak{a})$.

Proof. It has already been shown that $\mathfrak{a} \subset \mathfrak{a}'' \subset \mathfrak{I}(\mathfrak{a})$. In view of the description of $\mathfrak{I}(\mathfrak{a})$ as the coarsest topology on S that contains $\mathfrak{a}$, it will suffice to prove that $\mathfrak{a}''$ is a topology. $\mathfrak{a}''$ satisfies (O_1); for if

$\mathcal{B}$ is any subcollection of $\mathcal{Q}''$, each $X \in \mathcal{B}$ is of the form $\cup \mathcal{C}_X$, where $\mathcal{C}_X$ is a subcollection of $\mathcal{Q}'$. Let $\mathcal{C} = \cup \{\mathcal{C}_X : X \in \mathcal{B}\}$; as the union of a collection of subcollections of $\mathcal{Q}'$, $\mathcal{C}$ itself is a subcollection of $\mathcal{Q}'$. Moreover,

$$\cup \mathcal{B} = \cup \{X : X \in \mathcal{B}\} = \cup \{\cup \mathcal{C}_X : X \in \mathcal{B}\} = \cup \mathcal{C} \in \mathcal{Q}''.$$

Here the last equality follows from the general associative law for unions (*Sets*, 11). $\mathcal{Q}''$ also satisfies (O_2). Let $\mathcal{B}$ be a nonempty finite subcollection of $\mathcal{Q}''$. Again, each member X of $\mathcal{B}$ is the union of some subcollection $\mathcal{C}_X$ of $\mathcal{Q}'$. Then, because forming finite intersections is distributive over forming unions (*Sets*, 15),

$$\cap \mathcal{B} = \cap \{\cup \mathcal{C}_X : X \in \mathcal{B}\} = \cup \{\cap \mathcal{D} : \mathcal{D} \text{ has just one element}$$
in common with each $\mathcal{C}_X\}$.

Each collection $\mathcal{D}$ consists of sets which are intersections of nonempty finite subcollections of $\mathcal{Q}$. If one applies the associative law for intersections here just as its counterpart for unions was applied in the verification of (O_1), the conclusion is that $\cap \mathcal{D}$ itself is the intersection of a nonempty finite subcollection of $\mathcal{Q}$; so $\cap \mathcal{D} \in \mathcal{Q}'$. Therefore $\cap \mathcal{B}$ belongs to $\mathcal{Q}''$, and this is what had to be shown. Finally, $\mathcal{Q}''$ satisfies (O_3) because $S \in \mathcal{Q} \subset \mathcal{Q}''$.

Because of Theorem 9, a sub-base of a topology $\mathcal{3}$ can also be defined as a subcollection $\mathcal{Q}$ of $\mathcal{3}$ with the property that every set belonging to $\mathcal{3}$ is the union of some collection of intersections of nonempty finite subcollections of $\mathcal{Q} \cup \{S\}$.

From the constructive point of view, the approach to $\mathcal{3}(\mathcal{Q})$ afforded by Theorem 9 may seem to be no very great improvement over the definition itself; but it often supplies a good deal of insight into the character of $\mathcal{3}(\mathcal{Q})$ when the definition does not. This is illustrated by the following example. A subset of R^2 of the form $\{(x, y) : ax + by < c\}$, where a, b, and c are real numbers, and a and b are not both 0, is called an *open half-plane*. What is the coarsest topology that can be assigned to R^2 so that the open half-planes are indeed open? In other words, if $\mathcal{Q}$ is the collection of all open half-planes, what is $\mathcal{3}(\mathcal{Q})$? In the notation used earlier, $\mathcal{Q}'$ in this case is the collection consisting of the empty set, R^2, and all "open convex polygons"—interiors of convex figures bounded by "broken lines." According to Theorem 9, $\mathcal{3}(\mathcal{Q})$ must therefore consist of all sets that are unions of collections of such "open convex polygons." One can show that a subset of R^2 is the union of some collection of "open convex polygons" if and only if it is the union of some collections of 2-cells, so $\mathfrak{I}(\mathfrak{a})$ turns out to be the standard topology on R^2.

Exercises

74. Find a sub-base with as few members as possible for each of the following topologies on $S = \{a, b, c\}$. (a) $\{\emptyset, \{a\}, S\}$; (b) $\{\emptyset, \{a\}, \{b, c\}, S\}$; (c) $\{\emptyset, \{a\}, \{a, b\}, \{a, c\}, S\}$; (d) the discrete topology.

75. Prove that if $\mathfrak{a}$ generates the topology $\mathfrak{I}$, then any collection $\mathfrak{a}_1$ that satisfies $\mathfrak{a} \subset \mathfrak{a}_1 \subset \mathfrak{I}$ also generates $\mathfrak{I}$.

76. Let S be any nonempty set and let $\mathfrak{a}$ be the collection of subsets of S whose complements are singletons. Show that $\mathfrak{a}$ generates the cofinite topology on S.

77. Determine the topologies on R^2 generated by each of the following collections of subsets of R^2. (a) The collection of all straight lines; (b) the collection of all open half-planes of the special form $\{(x, y): x < c\}$; (c) the collection of all 2-cells of radius at least 1.

Bases. If $\mathfrak{I}$ is a topology, a subcollection $\mathfrak{B}$ of $\mathfrak{I}$ is called a *base* for $\mathfrak{I}$ if every member of $\mathfrak{I}$ is the union of some subcollection of $\mathfrak{B}$. Several simple examples are ready to hand. The collection of all n-cells in R^n is a base for the standard topology on R^n; if S is any nonempty set, $\{S\}$ is a base for the trivial topology on S, and the collection of all singletons of elements of S is a base for the discrete topology on S. Any topology is a base for itself; and if $\mathfrak{a}$ is a sub-base for $\mathfrak{I}$, the collection $\mathfrak{a}'$ (in the notation introduced before Theorem 9) is a base for $\mathfrak{I}$.

As these examples may suggest, any base for a topology is also a sub-base for that topology.

Proof. If $\mathfrak{B}$ is a base for $\mathfrak{I}$, and $\mathfrak{B}_1$ is the collection of unions of subcollections of $\mathfrak{B}$, then $\mathfrak{B}_1 = \mathfrak{I}$. At the same time, in the notation of the last section, $\mathfrak{B} \subset \mathfrak{B}'$, so $\mathfrak{I} = \mathfrak{B}_1 \subset \mathfrak{B}'' = \mathfrak{I}(\mathfrak{B})$. Because $\mathfrak{I}(\mathfrak{B})$ is the coarsest topology containing $\mathfrak{B}$, $\mathfrak{I} = \mathfrak{I}(\mathfrak{B})$, as claimed.

It is good to know some intrinsic conditions under which a collection of sets is a base. One such set of conditions is provided by Theorem 10.

THEOREM 10. A collection $\mathfrak{B}$ of subsets of a nonempty set S is a base for some topology on S if and only if $\mathfrak{B}$ satisfies

(B_1) If $X \in \mathfrak{B}$ and $Y \in \mathfrak{B}$, and $x \in X \cap Y$, there exists a $Z \in \mathfrak{B}$ such that $x \in Z \subset X \cap Y$;
(B_2) $\cup \mathfrak{B} = S$.

The proof of this theorem is not too difficult to be an exercise.

Theorem 10 supplies a particularly simple means of constructing topologies. Take any collection $\mathfrak{B}$ of subsets of S that satisfies (B_1) and (B_2); then the collection of unions of subcollections of $\mathfrak{B}$ is a topology. This was the way in which the standard topologies for the Euclidean spaces were defined in Chapter 2. Such trouble as there was arose in verifying (B_1).

The concept of a base can be localized by saying that a collection $\mathfrak{B}$ of open sets in $(S, \mathfrak{I})$ is a *base at* x (where $x \in S$) if for every neighborhood N of x, there exists a set X belonging to $\mathfrak{B}$ such that $x \in X \subset N$. A collection $\mathfrak{B}$ is a base for $\mathfrak{I}$ if and only if it is a base at every point of S.

Exercises

78. Which of the collections appearing as sub-bases in Exercises 76 and 77 are bases for the topologies they generate?

79. Prove that if $\mathfrak{B}$ is a base of $\mathfrak{I}$ and $\mathfrak{B} \subset \mathfrak{A} \subset \mathfrak{I}$, then $\mathfrak{A}$ is a base of $\mathfrak{I}$.

80. Two topology bases on the same set S are said to be *equivalent* if they generate the same topology. Find a simple direct way of testing bases for equivalence, and use your criterion to show that $\mathfrak{B}_1$, the collection of all 2-cells in R^2, is a base equivalent to $\mathfrak{B}_2$, the collection of all "open rectangles" in R^2—that is, sets of the form $\{(x, y): a < x < b$ and $c < y < d\}$, where a, b, c, and d may be any real numbers.

Fundamental Systems of Neighborhoods. The concept of a base for a topology has a close parallel in the theory of neighborhoods. If $(S, \mathfrak{I})$ is a topological space, and every point x of S is assigned a collection $\mathfrak{N}_x$ of its neighborhoods such that a set is a neighborhood of x if and only if it is a superset of some member of $\mathfrak{N}_x$, then the family (*Sets*, 31) of collections $(\mathfrak{N}_x : x \in S)$ is a *fundamental system of neighborhoods* in $(S, \mathfrak{I})$. For example, in R^n a fundamental system of neighborhoods is obtained by choosing $\mathfrak{N}_x$ to be the collection of all n-cells centered at x. In a discrete topological space, one can take $\mathfrak{N}_x = \{\{x\}\}$.

Any fundamental system of neighborhoods must satisfy the following conditions:

(FN_1) If $M \in \mathfrak{N}_x$ and $N \in \mathfrak{N}_x$, then $M \cap N$ contains some member of $\mathfrak{N}_x$.

(FN_2) If $X \in \mathfrak{N}_x$, then $x \in X$.

(FN_3) If $X \in \mathfrak{N}_x$, there exists a member Y of $\mathfrak{N}_x$ such that, for any y belonging to Y, some subset Z of X belongs to $\mathfrak{N}_y$.

Conditions (FN_1) and (FN_2) follow directly from (N_2) and (N_4) (p. 15); and (FN_3) may be shown as follows. If $X \in \mathfrak{N}_x$, then $x \prec X$. Therefore, by (N_5), there exists a set Y_1 such that $x \prec Y_1$ and $u \prec X$ if $u \in Y_1$. By the definition of a fundamental system of neighborhoods, there exists a member Y of $\mathfrak{N}_x$ such that $Y \subset Y_1$. If $y \in Y$, then $y \prec X$, so there exists a member Z of $\mathfrak{N}_y$ satisfying $Z \subset X$.

From (FN_1) and (FN_2) it follows that each of the collections $\mathfrak{N}_x$ is a filter base on S (*Sets*, 43).

The properties (FN_1)–(FN_3) precisely characterize fundamental systems of neighborhoods.

THEOREM 11. If $(\mathfrak{N}_x : x \in S)$ is a family of nonempty collections of subsets of a nonempty set S which satisfies (FN_1)–(FN_3), then it is a fundamental system of neighborhoods in exactly one topological space whose ground set is S.

The proof of this theorem is only sketched here, because it follows a pattern that is now familiar. In view of the connection between fundamental systems of neighborhoods and the neighborhood relation, the only possible neighborhood relation compatible with a given family $(\mathfrak{N}_x : x \in S)$ is that defined by:

$$x \prec X \text{ if and only if } N \subset X \text{ for some } N \in \mathfrak{N}_x.$$

The first task is to show that the relation $\prec$ so defined really is a neighborhood relation by showing that it has the characteristic properties (N_1)–(N_5). Once this is done, Theorem 2 guarantees the existence of a unique topology on S such that $\prec$ is the neighborhood relation in the resulting topological space. Finally, one must show that the family $(\mathfrak{N}_x : x \in S)$ is indeed a fundamental system of neighborhoods in that space.

Thus a fundamental system of neighborhoods uniquely determines the topology to which it corresponds. For a given topological space, however, there may be many different fundamental systems of neighborhoods. It has already been pointed out, for example, that one fundamental system of neighborhoods for R^2 is obtained by taking $\mathfrak{N}_x$ to be the collection of 2-cells centered at x; but another is obtained if $\mathfrak{N}_x$ is taken to be the collection of all open rectangles (see Exercise 80) to which x belongs. Other examples of fundamental systems of neighborhoods in R^2 should now suggest themselves.

It can be shown that Hausdorff's axioms (A)–(C) characterize fundamental systems of *open* neighborhoods. The weakness of his definition of a topological space—quite apart from the question of whether his axiom (D) is desirable—lies in the fact that, as the examples just mentioned indicate, many different fundamental systems of open neighborhoods may correspond to the same topology.

The next two theorems give useful criteria for adherence and continuity in terms of fundamental systems of neighborhoods. Again, the proofs are left as exercises.

THEOREM 12. If $(\mathfrak{N}_x : x \in S)$ is a fundamental system of neighborhoods in $(S, \mathfrak{I})$, and $X \subset S$, then x is an adherent point of X if and only if $X \cap N \neq \emptyset$ for every member N of $\mathfrak{N}_x$.

THEOREM 13. If $(\mathfrak{N}_{1,x} : x \in S_1)$ and $(\mathfrak{N}_{2,x} : x \in S_2)$ are fundamental systems of neighborhoods in $(S_1, \mathfrak{I}_1)$ and $(S_2, \mathfrak{I}_2)$ respectively, then a function $f : S_1 \to S_2$ is continuous at a point x of S_1 if and only if, for every Y belonging to $\mathfrak{N}_{2,f(x)}$, the set $f^{-1}(Y)$ contains some member of $\mathfrak{N}_{1,x}$.

Theorems 12 and 13, particularly when compared with Theorem 5 and the definition of continuity respectively, exemplify a general phenomenon. Many of the purposes served by neighborhoods in general can be served about as well, and sometimes better, by the neighborhoods drawn from some specific fundamental system of neighborhoods. For example, the fundamental system of neighborhoods for R^2 mentioned in the first paragraph of this section together with Theorem 12 gives the following criterion for denseness: A set X is dense in R^2 if and only if there is at least one point of X in every 2-cell (that is, in every "fundamental neighborhood" of every point). This criterion for denseness is probably much easier to apply in specific cases than the definition of denseness itself or the criterion in terms of general neighborhoods that might be formulated on the basis of Theorem 5.

Exercises

81. Show that if $\mathfrak{N}_x = \{U : x \in U$ and $U \in \mathfrak{I}\}$, then $(\mathfrak{N}_x : x \in S)$ is a fundamental system of neighborhoods for $(S, \mathfrak{I})$.

82. Let S be the set R^1 of real numbers, and for each x in S let $\mathfrak{N}_x$ be the collection of all sets of the form $\{y : x \leq y < x_1\}$, where $x_1 > x$. Prove that $(\mathfrak{N}_x : x \in S)$ is a fundamental system of neighborhoods, and show that the corresponding topology is finer than the standard topology, coarser than the discrete topology, and different from both.

83. Prove Theorem 12.

84. Prove Theorem 13.

85. Write a detailed proof of Theorem 11.

Topologies Induced by Functions. The discussion of general methods for topologizing a set out of thin air, as it were, is now complete. The rest of this chapter deals with several basic methods for constructing new topological spaces from given ones. The first of these not only is important in itself but also provides a means for fitting most of the others into a common pattern.

A situation that occurs frequently is this: One has a nonempty set S, a topological space $(S_1, \mathfrak{I}_1)$, and some function $f: S \to S_1$, and one wants to assign a topology $\mathfrak{I}$ to S in such a way that f is $(\mathfrak{I}, \mathfrak{I}_1)$-continuous. This can always be done; $\mathfrak{I}$ could be chosen to be the discrete topology on S. Usually, however, it is both possible and desirable to solve the problem without going to such a brutal extreme. In fact, the objective is ordinarily to find a $\mathfrak{I}$ that is as coarse as possible.

According to Theorem 6, f is $(\mathfrak{I}, \mathfrak{I}_1)$-continuous if and only if $\mathcal{S} \subset \mathfrak{I}$, where

$$\mathcal{S} = \{f^{-1}(V): V \in \mathfrak{I}_1\}.$$

The appropriate choice for $\mathfrak{I}$ is therefore the coarsest topology on S that contains the collection $\mathcal{S}$—in other words, the topology generated by $\mathcal{S}$. In principle, this observation solves the problem. The situation is even simpler than it looks, however, because under these circumstances *the collection $\mathcal{S}$ is itself a topology*, so one should take $\mathfrak{I} = \mathcal{S}$. This follows easily from the properties of inverse images. For example, if $\mathcal{C}$ is any finite subcollection of $\mathcal{S}$, there exists a finite subcollection $\mathcal{C}_1$ of $\mathfrak{I}_1$ such that $\mathcal{C} = \{f^{-1}(V): V \in \mathcal{C}_1\}$. Then $\cap \mathcal{C} = f^{-1}(\cap \mathcal{C}_1)$ (*Sets*, 27), and since $\cap \mathcal{C}_1 \in \mathfrak{I}_1$, the set $f^{-1}(\cap \mathcal{C}_1) \in \mathcal{S}$. Thus $\cap \mathcal{C} \in \mathcal{S}$, so $\mathcal{S}$ satisfies (O_1). In much the same way it can be shown that $\mathcal{S}$ satisfies (O_2) and (O_3).

The topology $\mathfrak{I} = \{f^{-1}(V): V \in \mathfrak{I}_1\}$ is called *the topology induced on S by f and $\mathfrak{I}_1$*.

A natural extension of the problem arises when there is a family of functions from an untopologized set S into the ground sets of a family (with the same index set) of topological spaces and the goal is to topologize S as coarsely as possible so that all the functions in the family are continuous. Suppose that the given family of functions is $(f_\alpha: \alpha \in A)$, where A is some index set, and that the given family of topological spaces is denoted by $((S_\alpha, \mathfrak{I}_\alpha): \alpha \in A)$, where $f_\alpha: S \to S_\alpha$ for each α belonging to A. Some or all of the spaces $(S_\alpha, \mathfrak{I}_\alpha)$ may coincide; so, for that matter, may the functions f_α. The problem may now be described more precisely as that of assigning to S the coarsest topology $\mathfrak{I}$ such that for every index α, the function f_α is $(\mathfrak{I}, \mathfrak{I}_\alpha)$-continuous.

A line of reasoning like that just applied in the one-function case shows that the needed topology $\mathfrak{I}$ must be that generated by the collection of subsets of S

$$\mathcal{S} = \{f_\alpha^{-1}(V_\alpha) \colon \alpha \in A \text{ and } V_\alpha \in \mathfrak{I}_\alpha\} \, ;$$

that is, $\mathfrak{I}$ is the coarsest topology to which all sets of the form $f_\alpha^{-1}(V_\alpha)$ belong. In general, $\mathcal{S}$ is not a topology, so the process of generating $\mathfrak{I}$ may not end so soon as in the one-function case. The topology $\mathfrak{I}$ defined in this way is again said to be *induced* on S by the given families of functions and topologies (or spaces).

In practice, not all topologies are specified by this process, but surprisingly many standard methods of topologization can be regarded as this process in disguise. Situations of this kind are pointed out in various particular settings later.

The next theorem often makes it easier to give a direct description of induced topologies.

THEOREM 14.   If $\mathfrak{I}$ is the topology induced on S by the family of functions $(f_\alpha \colon \alpha \in A)$ and the family of spaces $((S_\alpha, \mathfrak{I}_\alpha) \colon \alpha \in A)$, and if, for each index α, the collection $\mathfrak{A}_\alpha$ is a sub-base for $\mathfrak{I}_\alpha$, then $\mathfrak{I}$ is generated by the collection

$$\mathfrak{A} = \{f_\alpha^{-1}(X_\alpha) \colon \alpha \in A \text{ and } X_\alpha \in \mathfrak{A}_\alpha\}.$$

Proof. Since $\mathfrak{A}_\alpha \subset \mathfrak{I}_\alpha$ for all α, the collection $\mathfrak{A}$ is contained in the collection $\mathcal{S}$. If the topologies generated by these two collections are called $\mathfrak{I}_0$ and $\mathfrak{I}$ respectively, then it follows at once that $\mathfrak{I}_0 \subset \mathfrak{I}$. Because $\mathfrak{I}$ is the coarsest topology containing $\mathcal{S}$, it will now suffice to show that $\mathcal{S}$ is contained in $\mathfrak{I}_0$. In fact, if $V_\alpha \in \mathfrak{I}_\alpha$, then because $\mathfrak{A}_\alpha$ is a sub-base of $\mathfrak{I}_\alpha$, the set V_α is the union of some collection of intersections of finite collections of sets X_α belonging to $\mathfrak{A}_\alpha$. Then, because of the properties of f_α^{-1}, the set $f_\alpha^{-1}(V_\alpha)$ is exactly the same combination of the sets $f_\alpha^{-1}(X_\alpha)$, and therefore belongs to the topology generated by $\mathfrak{A}$, namely $\mathfrak{I}_0$. This gives $\mathcal{S} \subset \mathfrak{I}_0$, as needed.

EXAMPLE.   Let S be the untopologized plane R^2, and let $\mathfrak{F}$ be the collection of all linear functions from R^2 into the Euclidean line R^1 with its standard topology. This $\mathfrak{F}$ can be treated as a self-indexed family $(f \colon f \in \mathfrak{F})$ (*Sets*, 31). (A function $f \colon R^2 \to R^1$ is linear if it satisfies $f(x, y) = ax + by$, where a and b are real numbers.) In the notation of Theorem 14, then, $(S_f, \mathfrak{I}_f) = R^1$ for every f belonging to $\mathfrak{F}$. It is easy to see that one sub-base for the standard topology on R^1 is the collection of all open half-lines, namely sets of the form $\{x \colon x < c\}$ or

$\{x: x > c\}$, where c may be any real number. Therefore, according to Theorem 14, the topology $\mathfrak{I}$ induced on R^2 in this case is that generated by the collection of sets of the form $f^{-1}(X)$, where f is linear and X is an open half-line. This collection, however, is just the collection of open half-planes in R^2. It has already been pointed out that this collection generates the standard topology on R^2, so it follows that the topology $\mathfrak{I}$ induced here is the standard topology.

Exercises

86. Let $S = \{1, 2, 3\}$, $S_1 = \{1, 2, 3, 4\}$, and $\mathfrak{I}_1 = \{\emptyset, \{1\}, \{1, 2\}, \{3, 4\}, \{1, 3, 4\}, S_1\}$. Find the topology induced on S by $\mathfrak{I}_1$ and the function $f: S \to S_1$ defined by $f(x) = x + 1$.

87. Let S be the set of real numbers, and let $f: S \to R^2$ be the function defined by $f(x) = (x, 2x)$. Describe the corresponding induced topology on S.

88. Show that every topology is induced; that is, for every topology there exist a function and a topology that induce it.

89. Take S to be untopologized R^2 and all the spaces $(S_x, \mathfrak{I}_x)$ to be R^1 with the standard topology, as in the example. Describe the induced topology on S when $\mathfrak{F}$ is taken to be each of the following collections (self-indexed families) of functions. (a) The collection of all constant functions from R^2 into R^1 (see Exercise 60); (b) the collection of all linear functions of the special form $f(x, y) = ax$, where a may be any real number; (c) the collection of all functions from R^2 into R^1.

Subspaces. If X is a nonempty set in a topological space $(S, \mathfrak{I})$, then, although X itself can normally be topologized in many ways which may or may not take $\mathfrak{I}$ into account, there is one topology that is especially useful. This is the *relative topology* $\mathfrak{I}_X$ defined by

$$\mathfrak{I}_X = \{X \cap U: U \in \mathfrak{I}\}.$$

The typical open set in $(X, \mathfrak{I}_X)$ is then merely that part of some open set in $(S, \mathfrak{I})$ which lies in X. When the subset X is topologized in this way, and only then, the resulting topological space is called a *subspace* of $(S, \mathfrak{I})$.

That the relative topology $\mathfrak{I}_X$ is indeed a topology on X may be verified directly by using some simple facts of set theory and the assumption that $\mathfrak{I}$ is a topology. A quicker and perhaps more illuminating way to do it is to observe that $\mathfrak{I}_X$ is precisely the topology induced on X by the injection map $j: X \to S$ (*Sets*, 25) and the topology $\mathfrak{I}$.

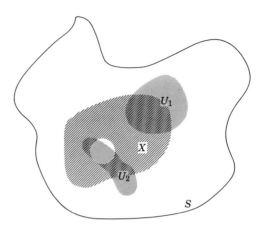

The relative topology

When dealing with subspaces one should be careful to specify whether such topological terms as "open," "derived set," and "closure," when applied to sets in a subspace, refer to the parent topology $\mathfrak{I}$ or to the relative topology, say $\mathfrak{I}_X$. It may easily happen, for example, that a subset Y of X may be open in the subspace $(X, \mathfrak{I}_X)$ but not in the parent space $(S, \mathfrak{I})$, as when $Y = X$ and $X \notin \mathfrak{I}$.

The following omnibus theorem gives some idea of how various topological properties and relationships in a subspace derive from those in the parent space.

THEOREM 15. If $(X, \mathfrak{I}_X)$ is a subspace of the topological space $(S, \mathfrak{I})$, then

(i) a subset A of X is closed in the subspace if and only if $A = X \cap F$, where F is some closed set in $(S, \mathfrak{I})$;

(ii) a subset N of X is a neighborhood of a point x in $(X, \mathfrak{I}_X)$ if and only if $N = X \cap M$, where M is a neighborhood of x in $(S, \mathfrak{I})$;

(iii) the closure in $(X, \mathfrak{I}_X)$ of a subset A of X is $X \cap \bar{A}$, where $\bar{A}$ is the closure of A in $(S, \mathfrak{I})$;

(iv) If $\mathfrak{A}$ is a sub-base [base] for $\mathfrak{I}$, then the collection $\mathfrak{A}_X$ defined by $\mathfrak{A}_X = \{X \cap V; V \in \mathfrak{A}\}$ is a sub-base [base] for $\mathfrak{I}_X$.

The list of parts of this theorem could be extended to include statements about interiors, cluster points, and so on. There are straightforward proofs of all these statements, and the following proof of (i) may do as a specimen: If A is closed in the subspace, then $A = X - (X \cap U)$, where $U \in \mathfrak{I}$. But $X - (X \cap U) = X - U = X \cap \complement U$. Thus $A = X \cap F$, where F is the closed [in $(S, \mathfrak{I})$] set $\complement U$. Conversely, if $A = X \cap F$, where $V = \complement F \in \mathfrak{I}$, then $A = X \cap (X - V) = X - (X \cap V)$, so A, as the complement in X of the set $X \cap V$ which belongs to $\mathfrak{I}_X$, is closed in $(X, \mathfrak{I}_X)$. Parts (ii), (iii), and (iv) of the theorem should be regarded as exercises.

Part (iv) of the theorem can simplify the task of recognizing relative topologies. For example, let X be the subset of the Euclidean plane R^2 consisting of all ordered pairs $(x, 0)$, where x is any real number. In a natural way—namely, by means of the one-to-one correspondence $x \leftrightarrow (x, 0)$—X can be viewed as a replica of R^1 embedded in R^2. Since the 2-cells form a base for the standard topology on R^2, and since, as a very short algebraic argument shows, the intersection of a 2-cell with X is either empty or a 1-cell, it follows from part (iv) of Theorem 15 that the relative topology on X is the one that has the collection of all 1-cells as a base, and this of course is just the standard topology on R^1.

The concept of a subspace is helpful in formulating a concept of continuity intermediate to continuity at a point and outright continuity. If $(S_1, \mathfrak{I}_1)$ and $(S_2, \mathfrak{I}_2)$ are topological spaces, and $f \colon S_1 \to S_2$, it would be quite in line with the terminology introduced at the beginning of Chapter 3 to say that f is continuous on a subset X of S_1 if it is continuous at every point x belonging to X. Part (ii) of Theorem 15 can be used to show that when X is open this is entirely equivalent to saying that the restriction

$$f | X \colon X \to S_2$$

of f to X (*Sets*, 26) is continuous, it being understood that X is assigned its relative topology. This point of view makes it possible to bring the content of Theorems 6 and 7 (among others) into play for continuity of this intermediate kind.

Another connection between the subspace concept and that of continuity is embodied in the next theorem, which is used more often than it is mentioned.

THEOREM 16. If $(S_1, \mathfrak{I}_1)$ and $(S_2, \mathfrak{I}_2)$ are topological spaces and $f \colon S_1 \to S_2$, and $f(S_1) \subset Y \subset S_2$, then f is $(\mathfrak{I}_1, \mathfrak{I}_2)$-continuous if and only if it is $(\mathfrak{I}_1, \mathfrak{I}_{2Y})$-continuous as a function from S_1 into Y.

From the definition of a function $f: S_1 \rightarrow S_2$ as a certain kind of subset of $S_1 \times S_2$, it appears that such a function is also a function $f: S_1 \rightarrow Y$ if Y is any set of the sort specified in the theorem. The symbol $\Im_{2Y}$ denotes the relative topology on Y in $(S_2, \Im_2)$. The essential point of the theorem is that the continuity of f does not depend on the situation in $S_2 - f(S_1)$.

Proof. Let $U \in \Im_2$. Then $f^{-1}(U) = f^{-1}(Y \cap U)$. Thus every $f^{-1}(U) \in \Im_1$ if and only if every $f^{-1}(Y \cap U) \in \Im_1$; that is, if and only if $f^{-1}(V) \in \Im_1$ whenever $V \in \Im_{2Y}$. The theorem then follows at once from the open set criterion for continuity supplied by Theorem 6.

Exercises

90. Describe in direct terms the relative topologies for the following sets in R^1. (*a*) The set of all integers; (*b*) the set $\{x: 0 < x < 1\}$; (*c*) the set of all reciprocals of positive integers.

91. Show that if $(X, \Im_X)$ is a subspace of $(S, \Im)$, then those subsets of X that are open in $(X, \Im_X)$ are exactly those that are open in $(S, \Im)$ if and only if $X \in \Im$.

92. Show that any two subspaces of R^2 with ground sets of the form $\{(x, y): ax + by + c = 0\}$ (where a, b, and c are fixed real numbers and a and b are not both zero) are homeomorphic.

Product Spaces. If $((S_\alpha, \Im_\alpha): \alpha \in A)$ is a family of topological spaces, it is reasonable to ask whether there is some promising way to use the topologies $\Im_\alpha$ to topologize the Cartesian product $S = \times_\alpha S_\alpha$ (*Sets*, 33).

The typical element of S is a family $x = (x_\alpha: \alpha \in A)$, where $x_\alpha \in S_\alpha$ for each α; and with this notation, the αth projection is the function $f_\alpha: S \rightarrow S_\alpha$ defined by $f_\alpha(x) = x_\alpha$. One rather simple desideratum for any useful topologization for S would be that all the projections should be continuous: For each index α, one would like to be able to say that if y is close to x, then y_α is close to x_α. If one imposes the additional desideratum that the topology on S should be no finer than it has to be to accomplish this, the desired topology on S is exactly the topology induced on S by $(f_\alpha: \alpha \in A)$ and $(\Im_\alpha: \alpha \in A)$, namely that generated by the collection

$$\mathcal{C} = \{f_\alpha^{-1}(V_\alpha): \alpha \in A, V_\alpha \in \Im_\alpha\}.$$

The topology $\Im$ generated by this collection is in fact the topology customarily assigned to S under these circumstances. It is called the *product topology*, and the topological space $(S, \mathfrak{I})$ is called the *topological product* of the family of topological spaces $((S_\alpha, \mathfrak{I}_\alpha): \alpha \in A)$.

Because of the importance of this concept, it will be worthwhile to examine the structure of the product topology in some detail.

According to the discussion at the beginning of this chapter, one base $\mathfrak{B}$ for the product topology would be the collection of all intersections of finite subcollections of $\mathfrak{C}$—that is, the collection of all sets of the form

$$f_{\alpha_1}^{-1}(V_{\alpha_1}) \cap f_{\alpha_2}^{-1}(V_{\alpha_2}) \cap \cdots \cap f_{\alpha_n}^{-1}(V_{\alpha_n}),$$

where each $\alpha_i \in A$ and $V_{\alpha_i} \in \mathfrak{I}_{\alpha_i}$. Since

$$f_{\alpha_i}^{-1}(V_{\alpha_i}) = \{x \in S: x_{\alpha_i} \in V_{\alpha_i}\},$$

the intersection just described can be regarded as the set of all elements of S of the form $x = (x_\alpha: \alpha \in A)$, where $x_\alpha \in S_\alpha$ and $x_{\alpha_i} \in V_{\alpha_i}(1 \leq i \leq n)$. But this in turn shows that the intersection is in fact $\times_\alpha V_\alpha$, where $V_\alpha \in \mathfrak{I}_\alpha$ for every α in A, and $V_\alpha = S_\alpha$ for all but a finite number of indices α. Thus the product topology is that topology on S which has as a base

$$\mathfrak{C}' = \{\times_\alpha V_\alpha: V_\alpha \in \mathfrak{I}_\alpha, \text{ and } V_\alpha = S_\alpha \text{ for almost all } \alpha\}.$$

Here "for almost all α" is short for "for all α, with a finite number of exceptions," as is customary in such cases. If the index set A is finite, then the stipulation "$V_\alpha = S_\alpha$ for almost all α" is redundant, and may be dropped from the description of $\mathfrak{C}'$.

As might be expected, the topological product of any but the simplest families of topological spaces confronts the imagination with a high hurdle, and it is often necessary to work with topological products on a formal basis without much help from the intuition. Nevertheless, a knowledge of several moderately simple examples will provide some basis for an understanding of the general idea.

R^2 AS A TOPOLOGICAL PRODUCT. If $(S_1, \mathfrak{I}_1)$ and $(S_2, \mathfrak{I}_2)$ are both taken to be the 1-dimensional Euclidean space with the standard topology, then $S = S_1 \times S_2 = R^2$. Since the collection of open intervals is a base for the standard topology on R^1, Exercise 95 justifies saying that the collection of all sets of the form $B_1 \times B_2$, where each B_i is either an open interval or the whole ground set $R^1(= S_1 = S_2)$, is a base for the product topology. In geometrical language, the typical element of this base is either an "open rectangle" (see Exercise 80), an "open vertical strip," an "open horizontal strip"—the last two terms should be sufficiently self-explanatory—or the whole plane. Because the plane, as well as any open strip of either type, is the union of a collection of open rectangles, one can go farther and say that the collection of open rectangles is already a base for the product topology. According to Exercise 80, however, the collection of open rectangles is a base for the standard topology on R^2; thus the product topology is simply the standard topology.

Reasoning in exactly the same way, one can show that for any positive integer n, the n-dimensional Euclidean space R^n is the topological product of n copies of R^1. There is no theoretical obstacle to prevent one from going on and considering the topological product of an infinite family of copies of R^1, but then one must forego the simplifications of the general definition that depend on the finiteness of the index set A.

THE CIRCULAR CYLINDER. The subspace of R^2 whose ground set is $\{(x, y) : x^2 + y^2 = 1\}$ may be called the *unit circle C*. The standard topology on C is then the relative topology on C obtained from the standard topology on R^2. Using part (iv) of Theorem 15 and some elementary geometry, one can show that one base for the standard topology on C is the collection of all open arcs, that is, sets of the form

$$\{(\cos \vartheta, \sin \vartheta) : \alpha < \vartheta < \beta\},$$

where α and β are real numbers. The topological product of C and R^1 is the *circular cylinder*. It may be shown that this is homeomorphic to the subspace of R^3 whose ground set is $\{(x, y, z) : x^2 + y^2 = 1\}$—hence the name. The definite article is justified by the fact that any circular cylinder in the ordinary geometrical sense is (as a subspace of R^3) homeomorphic to the topological product of C and R^1.

Exercises

93. Choose as $(S_1, \mathfrak{I}_1)$ and $(S_2, \mathfrak{I}_2)$ any two specific nonhomeomorphic topological spaces with three-element ground sets (Exercises 6 and 71) and find the product topology explicitly.

94. Show that the product topology for a family of discrete topological spaces, each of which has at least two points, is discrete if and only if the family (that is, its index set) is finite.

95. Show that if $((S_\alpha, \mathfrak{I}_\alpha) : \alpha \in A)$ is a family of topological spaces, and for each index α the collection $\mathfrak{B}_\alpha$ is a base for $\mathfrak{I}_\alpha$, then the collection of all sets of the form $\times_\alpha B_\alpha$, where $B_\alpha \in \mathfrak{B}_\alpha$ for finitely many

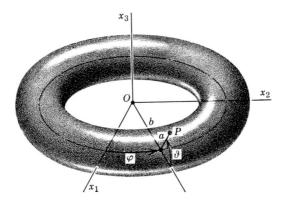

A torus

indices α and $B_\alpha = S_\alpha$ for all other indices, is a base for the product topology on $S = \times_\alpha S_\alpha$.

∗96. Show that the topological product of the unit circle C with itself is homeomorphic to a torus, namely the subspace of R^3 whose ground set is $\{((b + a \cos \vartheta) \cos \varphi, (b + a \cos \vartheta) \sin \varphi, a \sin \vartheta): 0 \le \vartheta < 2\pi, 0 \le \vartheta < 2\pi\}$ where $0 < a < b$ (see the figure).

The Cantor Discontinua. The so-called Cantor discontinua provide a further and somewhat deeper illustration of the topological product construction. A topological space whose ground set has exactly two elements and whose topology is discrete may be called a *couple*. The topological product of any family of couples is called a *(generalized) Cantor discontinuum*. When the index set is finite, the corresponding Cantor discontinuum is just a discrete space with a finite number of points (see Exercise 94); but when the index set is infinite, matters become more interesting. The rest of this section will be restricted to the case in which the index set is Z^+, the set of positive integers, but larger index sets also lead to important Cantor discontinua.

Since any two couples are certainly homeomorphic, it is safe to act as if all couples have the same ground set, say $\{0, 2\}$—the reason for this curious choice appears shortly. The typical element of the product set is then merely an ordinary infinite sequence (*Sets*, 32) in which each term is either 0 or 2. According to the general discussion in the preceding section, the product topology is that topology $\mathcal{3}$ on $S = \times_n S_n$ ($S_n = \{0, 2\}$) which has for a base the collection of all sets of the form $\times_n X_n$, where $X_n \subset \{0, 2\}$ for all $n \in Z^+$ and $X_n = \{0, 2\}$ for almost all n.

Improbable as it may seem, the space $(S, \mathfrak{I})$ is homeomorphic to a subspace of the Euclidean line R^1. The ground set for this subspace may be taken to be T, the set consisting of all real numbers which are sums of infinite series $\sum\limits_n x_n 3^{-n}$, where each x_n is either 0 or 2. In other words, T is the set of all real numbers from 0 to 1 inclusive whose "decimal" expansions to the base 3, $0 . x_1 x_2 \cdots x_n \cdots$, do not use the digit 1. This in turn suggests another description of T: It is the set obtained from the unit interval $\{x \in R^1 : 0 \leq x \leq 1\}$ by removing the open middle third $\{x : \frac{1}{3} < x < \frac{2}{3}\}$—this takes out all numbers for which $x_1 = 1$ in the expansion—then removing the open middle third from each of the two remaining pieces, so that all numbers for which $x_2 = 1$ are removed, and so on ad infinitum. Because of this description, the set T is sometimes called the (Cantor) *middle third set*, or the (Cantor) *ternary set*.

T with its relative topology is homeomorphic to the Cantor discontinuum. The natural homeomorphism $f : S \to T$ is defined by

$$f[(x_n : n \in Z^+)] = \sum\limits_n x_n 3^{-n}.$$

This formula certainly defines a function from S onto T. Less self-evidently than it may seem, f is one-to-one. The question of continuity comes next. For each $\xi = \sum\limits_n x_n 3^{-n} \in T$ and each $n_o \in Z^+$, let

$$W_{n_o}(\xi) = \{\xi' = \sum\limits_n x_n' 3^{-n} : x_n' = x_n \text{ if } n \leq n_o\}.$$

The construction of the Cantor set T

Then if $\mathfrak{N}_\xi = \{W_{n_o}(\xi) : n_o \in Z^+\}$, the family $(\mathfrak{N}_\xi : \xi \in T)$ is a fundamental system of neighborhoods for the relative topology on T. In much the same way, if $x = (x_n : n \in Z^+) \in S$, and $V_{n_o}(x) = \times_n Y_n$, where $Y_n = \{x_n\}$ if $n \le n_o$ and $Y_n = \{0, 2\}$ if $n > n_o$, and if $\mathfrak{M}_x = \{V_{n_o}(x) : n_0 \in Z^+\}$, then $(\mathfrak{M}_x : x \in S)$ is a fundamental system of neighborhoods for the product topology $\mathfrak{I}$ on S. With the help of Theorem 13 and the fact that f is a one-to-one correspondence, it follows from the identity

$$f[V_{n_o}(x)] = W_{n_o}[f(x)]$$

that f and f^{-1} are continuous, and therefore that f is a homeomorphism.

The Cantor ternary set is a favorite example for illustrating the unexpected. Again and again it can be brought forward as a counter-example against extremely plausible conjectures. It would not be dishonorable to guess, for example, that in so well-behaved a space as R^1 the derived set of any nowhere dense set should be empty; but Exercises 97–99 show, thanks to the Cantor ternary set, that this is false.

Exercises
97. Prove that the Cantor ternary set T is closed in R^1.
98. Prove that T°, the interior of T, is empty, and hence that T is nowhere dense in R^1.
99. Prove that T is perfect (see Exercise 32).

Quotient Spaces. A third basic construction used to obtain new topological spaces from old is that of forming quotient spaces.

If $(S, \mathfrak{I})$ is a given topological space, and E is an equivalence relation on S, then there is the quotient set S/E, the set whose elements are the equivalence classes in S determined by E (*Sets*, 34, 35). The problem is to use $\mathfrak{I}$ to define, in some straightforward way, a topology on this quotient set. Here again, the problem is solved by reference to making a certain function continuous, but in a way somewhat different from that used in the earlier constructions.

Any element of S belongs to exactly one element of S/E (that is, to one equivalence class); the relation f from S to S/E defined by "$f(x)$ is that element of S/E to which x belongs" is therefore a function from S onto S/E. This function is called the *natural mapping* from S onto S/E. According to the remarks preceding Theorem 7, if f is continuous when a certain topology $\mathfrak{I}'$ is assigned to S/E, then it will also be continuous if $\mathfrak{I}'$ is replaced by any coarser topology; and f will certainly be continuous if S/E is assigned the trivial topology. Thus it is natural to look for the *finest* topology on S/E for which f is continuous. The search does not last long; such a finest topology must be contained in the collection $\{Y \subset S/E : f^{-1}(Y) \in \Im\}$, and this collection is itself a topology. Therefore, given S, $\Im$, and E, one defines the collection $\Im_E = \{Y \subset S/E : f^{-1}(Y) \in \Im\}$ to be the *quotient topology* on S/E, and $(S/E, \Im_E)$ is the corresponding *quotient space*. One sometimes says that the quotient space is obtained by *identifying* the points in the various equivalence classes.

In principle, it is easy enough to recognize an open set in the quotient space. If $Y \subset S/E$, then Y is a collection of equivalence classes in S, and $f^{-1}(Y)$, which is

$$\{x \in S : f(x) \in y \text{ for some } y \in Y\},$$

is simply the union of Y in S. Therefore, *a set $Y \subset S/E$ is open in the quotient space if and only if its union is open in the given space* $(S, \Im)$.

A simple example or two may clarify matters. For the first example, let $(S, \Im)$ be 1-dimensional Euclidean space R^1, and let E be the equivalence relation $\{(x, y) : x - y \text{ is an integer}\}$. The typical equivalence class, then, is a set of the form $\{x + n : n \in Z\}$, where x is some real number and Z is the set of all integers. Since each equivalence class contains exactly one number y which satisfies $0 \le y < 1$, each equivalence class may be labeled by that number y which belongs to it and satisfies this inequality. In order to avoid ambiguity, a prime ($'$) will be attached to the real numbers used in this way; for example, $\frac{1}{2}' = \{\frac{1}{2} + n : n \in Z\}$; $0'$ is the set of all integers.

Now by working with the usual open-interval base of the standard topology on R^1, one can show that a base for the quotient topology in this case is the collection of all subsets of S/E of the form $\{y' : a < y < b\}$ or of the form $\{y' : 0 \le y < a \text{ or } b < y < 1\}$, where in either case a and b are real numbers satisfying $0 < a < b < 1$. Note that the topology $\Im_E$ which has just been defined is coarser than the relative topology that would be assigned to S/E if the latter were regarded, in the natural way, as a subset of R^1. More precisely, the function $f : \{y \in R^1 : 0 \le y < 1\} \to S/E$ defined by $f(y) = y'$ is continuous (and certainly one-to-one and onto), but it is not a homeomorphism. If $X = \{y : 0 \le y < \frac{1}{3}\}$, for example, then this set is open in $\{y \in R^1 : 0 \le y < 1\}$ with its relative topology, but $f(X)$ does not belong to the quotient topology. The essential difference between the two topologies can be indicated in the language of Chapter 2 by saying that in the quotient space any set $\{y' : a < y\}$, where $0 < a < 1$, contains points arbitrarily close to $0'$, although for the relative topology the corresponding statement is false.

Another way of arriving at the same example or, strictly speaking, a space homeomorphic to this one is first to take the subspace of R^1 whose ground set is the interval $\{y: 0 \leq y \leq 1\}$, and then to form the quotient space determined by the equivalence relation associated with the partition $\{\{0, 1\}, \{y: 0 < y < 1\}\}$ (*Sets*, 37).

This point of view is rather typical; that is, topological spaces are often constructed by first taking a subspace of some known topological space and then forming a quotient space from it by use of an equivalence relation specified by way of its associated partition. Here is another example of this kind: Let $(S, \mathfrak{I})$ be the subspace of R^2 whose ground set is the square $\{(x, y): |x| \leq 1, |y| \leq 1\}$. An equivalence relation E on S is defined by requiring the associated partition to consist of the following subsets of S: (i) singleton sets of points belonging to the open square $\{(x, y): |x| < 1, |y| < 1\}$; (ii) pairs of the form $\{(-1, y), (1, y)\}$, where $|y| < 1$; (iii) pairs of the form $\{(x, -1), (-x, 1)\}$, where $|x| < 1$; (iv) the set $\{(-1, -1), (1, -1), (-1, 1), (1, 1)\}$. In this case the quotient space $(S/E, \mathfrak{I}_E)$ is called the *Klein bottle*. This topological space has a number of diverting properties which are often mentioned in popular accounts of topology. Many such accounts describe the Klein bottle as the result of taking a square or rectangle and "pasting" its edges together in a certain way; this "pasting" is represented here by the identification, or herding into

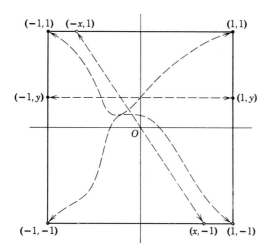

Construction of the Klein bottle

equivalence classes, of the boundary points of the square; two points are "pasted" together if, and only if, they belong to the same equivalence class. Most such "scissors and paste" constructions of surfaces can be regarded as applications of the quotient space concept.

Exercises

100. Let $(S, \mathfrak{I})$ be R^2, and define an equivalence relation E on S by saying that $((x_1, y_1), (x_2, y_2)) \in E$ if and only if $y_1 = y_2$. Show that $(S/E, \mathfrak{I}_E)$ is homeomorphic to R^1.

101. More generally, let $(S, \mathfrak{I})$ be the topological product of $(S_1, \mathfrak{I}_1)$ and $(S_2, \mathfrak{I}_2)$, and define E as in Exercise 100. Prove that $(S/E, \mathfrak{I}_E)$ is homeomorphic to $(S_1, \mathfrak{I}_1)$.

102. Show that the quotient space defined in the first example of this section is homeomorphic to the unit circle C (p. 58).

Metric Spaces. One further way of topologizing a set is to assign a suitably chosen "distance" to each pair of its points, and then to define a topology in terms of this distance. This leads back to Fréchet's original concept of a metric space, briefly discussed in Chapter 1. A more general version of the same approach to topologization is presented at length later in the book, but taking up metric spaces proper at this relatively early stage has its advantages.

A *metric*, or *distance function*, on a nonempty set S is a function d from $S \times S$ to R, the set of real numbers, which satisfies the following conditions:

(M_1) For any elements x and y of S, $d(x, y) \geq 0$; and $d(x, y) = 0$ if and only if $x = y$.
(M_2) For any elements x and y of S, $d(x, y) = d(y, x)$.
(M_3) For any elements x, y, and z of S,
$$d(x, y) \leq d(x, z) + d(z, y).$$

The conditions (M_1)–(M_3) reflect familiar properties of distance as it is ordinarily defined in Euclidean geometry. In particular, the property (M_3) corresponds to the fact that in any triangle the length of one side is always less than or equal to the sum of the lengths of the other two, even when the triangle is degenerate in the sense that the vertices are collinear. Condition (M_3) is therefore often called the *triangle axiom*.

A *metric space* is an ordered pair (S, d) in which S is a nonempty set and d is a metric on S.

If (S, d) is a metric space, a *natural topology* $\mathfrak{I}_d$ on S can be defined in various equivalent ways in terms of d. The pattern set by the discussion of the Euclidean spaces in Chapter 2 is followed here. If α is any positive real number and $x \in S$, the set

$$C(x, \alpha) = \{y \in S : d(x, y) < \alpha\}$$

is called the *open ball* of center x and radius α. The collection of all open balls in (S, d) will be denoted by $\mathcal{S}_d$. The topology generated by $\mathcal{S}_d$ is the *natural topology* $\mathfrak{I}_d$ for (S, d).

In fact, $\mathcal{S}_d$ is a base for $\mathfrak{I}_d$. This may be shown by verifying that $\mathcal{S}_d$ satisfies the conditions (B_1) and (B_2) of Theorem 10. It follows directly from (M_1) that $x \in C(x, \alpha)$ for any element x of S and any positive real number α; and from this in turn it follows that $\mathcal{S}_d$ satisfies (B_2). Now let $C(x_1, \alpha_1)$ and $C(x_2, \alpha_2)$ be any two open balls, and let $x \in C(x_1, \alpha_1) \cap C(x_2, \alpha_2)$. By the definition of open balls, this means that $d_1 = d(x_1, x) < \alpha_1$ and $d_2 = d(x_2, x) < \alpha_2$. If α is the smaller of the two positive numbers $\alpha_1 - d_1$ and $\alpha_2 - d_2$, and if $y \in C(x, \alpha)$, then $d(x, y) < \alpha$, and by (M_2) and (M_3),

$$d(x_i, y) \leq d(x_i, x) + d(x, y) < d_i + \alpha \leq \alpha_i,$$

so $y \in C(x_i, \alpha_i)$; here $i = 1$ or 2. Thus $C(x, \alpha) \subset C(x_i, \alpha_i)$, and this gives

$$C(x, \alpha) \subset C(x_1, \alpha_1) \cap C(x_2, \alpha_2),$$

in confirmation of (B_1).

In a metric space, therefore, a set belongs to the natural topology if and only if it is the union of some collection of open balls.

Like most of the other topologies constructed in this chapter, the natural topology can be regarded as a topology induced by functions. In fact, for each element x of S one can define a function $d_x : S \to R^1$ by the formula $d_x(y) = d(x, y)$; d_x might appropriately be called "the distance from x." The natural topology $\mathfrak{I}_d$ is just the topology induced on S by the family of functions $(d_x : x \in S)$ and, of course, the standard topology on R^1.

When topological concepts are used in connection with a metric space, it is taken as a matter of course, unless something is said to the contrary, that the topology concerned is $\mathfrak{I}_d$. In other words, one often speaks of a metric space (S, d) as if it were the topological space $(S, \mathfrak{I}_d)$. It is in this sense that metric spaces constitute a particular class of topological spaces.

A number of examples of metric spaces are given at the end of the chapter. This section concludes with one more general observation.

THEOREM 17.   If (S, d) is a metric space, and for each element x of S there is given a set I_x of positive real numbers for which 0 (in R^1) is a cluster point, and if

$$\mathfrak{N}_x = \{C(x, \alpha): \alpha \in I_x\},$$

then $(\mathfrak{N}_x: x \in S)$ is a fundamental system of neighborhoods in (S, d).

Proof.   Clearly, each $\mathfrak{N}_x$ consists of neighborhoods of x. If N is any neighborhood of x, then there exists an element y of R and a positive number γ such that $x \in C(y, \gamma) \subset N$. As in the verification of (B_1) given above, there must exist a positive number β for which $C(x, \beta) \subset C(y, \gamma)$. Since 0 is a cluster point of I_x, there is some element α of I_x which is less than β; then $x \in C(x, \alpha) \subset N$, and since $C(x, \alpha) \in \mathfrak{N}_x$, this finishes the proof.

In applications of this theorem, the set chosen to play the role of I_x is probably most often the set of reciprocals of the positive integers, $\{1/n: n \in Z^+\}$.

Exercises

103. If d is a metric on $\{a, b, c\}$ for which $d(a, b) = d(a, c) = 1$, what are the possible values of $d(b, c)$?

104. Prove that if (S, d) is a metric space, and $\{x_1, \ldots, x_n\}$ is any nonempty finite subset of S, then

$$d(x_1, x_n) \le \sum_{k=1}^{n} d(x_k, x_{k-1}).$$

105. Show that the list of conditions (M_1)–(M_3) is equivalent to the shorter list:

   (L_1) For any elements x and y of S, $d(x, y) = 0$ if and only if $x = y$.

   (L_2) For any elements x, y, and z of S,
   $$d(x, y) \le d(x, z) + d(y, z).$$

Metrizability and the Metrization Problem.   Different metrics on a given set S may define the same natural topology on S. This phenomenon can be illustrated by means of Example 2 in the next section, where the natural topology is the same (namely, the discrete topology) no matter how the constant α is chosen, although different choices give what are strictly speaking different metrics. A more interesting illustration is provided by the observation (Exercise 106) that if d is a metric on S, then the function d' defined by

$$d'(x, y) = \frac{d(x, y)}{1 + d(x, y)}$$

is also a metric on S, and defines the same natural topology as d. What makes this illustration interesting is that irrespective of the nature of S and d, the metric space (S, d') is *bounded* in the sense that there exists a constant M (M can be 1 in this case) such that $d'(x, y) \leq M$ for all elements x and y of S. Thus "boundedness" is not a topological property, for under these circumstances the spaces (S, d) and (S, d') are homeomorphic—the simplest homeomorphism is the identity map on S—but the latter space is bounded, while the former may easily be unbounded.

Having seen that a given topology may be the natural topology corresponding to a variety of metrics, one may wonder whether there are topologies which are not the natural topologies for any metrics at all. Sharpened somewhat, this problem may be formulated as follows: A topological space $(S, \mathfrak{I})$ is *metrizable* if these exists a metric d on S such that $\mathfrak{I} = \mathfrak{I}_d$. Do there exist nonmetrizable topological spaces? If so, what purely topological properties of a space are necessary and/or sufficient for metrizability?

The first of these two questions is easily answered, and the answer is yes. Thus the topological space concept really is more general than the metric space concept. For instance, any topological space whose ground set is finite and whose topology is not discrete is nonmetrizable. This amounts to saying that for every metric space with a finite ground set the natural topology must be discrete. In fact, if x is any point in such a space, and α_x is any positive real number such that $d(x, y) > \alpha_x$ for all points y belonging to $S - x$ [there exists such a number because of (M_1) and the finiteness of $S - \{x\}$], then $C(x, \alpha_x) = \{x\}$, so every singleton set, and therefore every set, in the space belongs to $\mathfrak{I}_d$.

The second question, about the existence of purely topological conditions for metrizability, is the famous *metrization problem*, which was first raised about 1920 and has been intensively studied since then. The problem was finally given a satisfactory solution in the early 1950's, when R. H. Bing, J. Nagata, and Yu. M. Smirnov, working independently, found relatively simple criteria for metrizability. Their results are not described here.*

---

* For information on this question, see R. H. Bing, "Metrization of Topological Spaces," *Canadian Journal of Mathematics*, **3**, 175–186 (1951); Yu. M. Smirnov, "On Metrization of Topological Spaces," *American Mathematical Society Translations*, Series 1, **8**, 62–77 (1962).

Exercises

106. Show that the function d' defined in the first paragraph of this section is indeed a metric.

*107. If $\mathfrak{I}_1$ and $\mathfrak{I}_2$ are topologies on the same set S, their *supremum* is defined as the smallest topology on S that contains them both; that is, the supremum is the topology generated by the collection $\mathfrak{I}_1 \cup \mathfrak{I}_2$. Show that the supremum of two metrizable topologies is metrizable.

Examples of Metric Spaces. Many of the important topological spaces of mathematics are in fact metrizable, and are often treated as metric spaces. The following examples, although certainly not exhaustive, will confirm this observation.

EXAMPLE 1. R^n, n-dimensional Euclidean space, is metrizable in a very direct way. If $x = (x_1, \ldots, x_n)$ and $y = (y_1, \ldots, y_n)$ are any two points of R^n, $d(x, y)$ may be taken to be the number

$$(\sum_{k=1}^{n} (x_k - y_k)^2)^{\frac{1}{2}}.$$

In the corresponding metric space, the open balls are precisely the n-cells discussed in Chapter 2, and $\mathfrak{I}_d$ is precisely the "standard topology" defined there. It is easy to see that this d satisfies (M_1) and (M_2), and the discussion in Chapter 2 provides the essentials of a proof that it satisfies (M_3). There are many other simple metrics on R^n that give the same natural topologies as d; for example, that defined by

$$d'(x, y) = \sum_{k=1}^{n} |x_k - y_k|.$$

EXAMPLE 2. Any discrete topological space is metrizable. If S is any nonempty set, and α is any positive constant, one can define a metric d_α on S by putting $d_\alpha(x, y) = \alpha$ if $x \neq y$, and $d_\alpha(x, y) = 0$ if $x = y$. Since, in the resulting metric space, $C(x, \alpha/2) = \{x\}$ for any element x of S, $\mathfrak{I}_{d_\alpha}$ is the discrete topology.

EXAMPLE 3. If S is a collection of bounded functions from any fixed set D into R^1, and for any f and g belonging to S, one puts $d(f, g) = \sup \{|f(x) - g(x)| : x \in D\}$ (*Sets*, 47), then (S, d) is a metric space. The natural topology $\mathfrak{I}_d$ in this case is sometimes called *the topology of uniform convergence* or simply the *sup* (pronounced "soup") *topology*.

EXAMPLE 4. If P is the set of rational numbers, and p is a fixed prime integer, a metric d_p on P is defined if one sets $d_p(x, y) = 0$ when

$x = y$, and when $x \neq y$ sets $d_p(x, y)$ equal to that power p^n of p for which the rational number $p^n(x - y)$ may be represented as a fraction in which neither numerator nor denominator is divisible by p. The metric space (P, d_p) is of importance in algebraic number theory.

EXAMPLE 5. If (S, d) is any metric space, and X is a nonempty subset of S, then the restriction $d|(X \times X)$ is a metric on X; thus if this restriction is denoted by d_X, the pair (X, d_X) is a metric space, called a (metric) *subspace* of the given space. This definition does not, in itself, constitute an example of a metric space, but it does provide a means of constructing innumerable examples from given examples.

EXAMPLE 6. Let $((S_k, d_k): k = 1, 2, \ldots, n)$ be any finite family of metric spaces. If $x = (x_1, x_2, \ldots, x_n)$ and $y = (y_1, y_2, \ldots, y_n)$ are any elements of the Cartesian product $S = \times_k S_k$, define

$$d(x, y) = (\sum_k [d_k(x_k, y_k)]^2)^{\frac{1}{2}}.$$

The function d is a metric on S, called the *product metric;* and the metric space (S, d) is the (metric) *product* of the given family of metric spaces. [Some writers prefer to define the product metric by

$$d(x, y) = \sum_k d_k(x_k, y_k),$$

but the results are essentially the same.] This again is not so much an example as a means of constructing examples from others.

Exercises. Exercises 108–113 are respectively the problems of showing that the metrics defined in Examples 1–6 are in fact metrics—that is, that they satisfy (M_1)–(M_3).

114. In terms of Example 5, prove that the natural topology for (X, d_X) is the relative topology on X obtained from the natural topology for (S, d).

115. In terms of Example 6, prove that the natural topology for (S, d) is the product topology corresponding to the given family of natural topologies.

CHAPTER FIVE

Separation, compactness, and connectedness

The concept of a topological space, if unrestricted, is too general for many purposes. To obtain certain highly desirable conclusions about some matters, restrictions that go beyond the basic (O_1)–(O_3) must be imposed on the spaces. The restrictions that can serve this purpose are numerous and diverse. Over the years, however, a few especially versatile restrictions have risen to a position of preeminence, and the topological spaces satisfying each of them—or certain combinations of them—form categories for which there are important special theories. In this chapter several of these standard restrictions and some of their implications are briefly considered.

Separation Axioms. It is easy to see (look at any trivial topological space with at least two points!) that not all topological spaces as defined in Chapter 2 satisfy Hausdorff's original axiom (D), quoted in Chapter 1. Nevertheless, it is often expedient to assume that a topological space satisfies that axiom, and in fact many important specific topological spaces do satisfy it. Indeed, there is a whole hierarchy of "axioms" of the same general character, and these have come to be called *separation axioms*.

It will simplify the task of formulating the separation axioms to introduce two new terms. If X and Y are sets in a topological space $(S, \mathfrak{I})$, X will be said to be *insulated** from Y if there exists a set $U \in \mathfrak{I}$ satisfying $X \subset U$ and $U \cap Y = \emptyset$; that is, if X has an open superset disjoint from Y. Moreover, X and Y are *separated* if there

---

* This term is not standard.

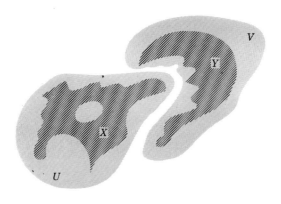

Separated sets

exist sets U and V belonging to $\mathfrak{I}$ such that $X \subset U$, $Y \subset V$, and $U \cap V = \emptyset$; that is, if X and Y have disjoint open supersets. In these circumstances U and V will be said to separate X and Y. Notice that being separated is a symmetric relation on $\mathcal{P}(S)$, but that being insulated is not symmetric in general.

The most commonly used separation axioms may now be listed; they are numbered more or less in accordance with the widely adopted scheme introduced by P. S. Aleksandrov and H. Hopf in their treatise *Topologie* I (Berlin, 1935).

(0) Of any two distinct singletons, at least one is insulated from the other.

(I) Any singleton is insulated from any other singleton.

(II) Any two distinct singletons are separated.

(III) Any closed set and any singleton not contained in it are separated.

(IV) Any two disjoint closed sets are separated.

In a sense, each of these axioms is more stringent than those that precede it in the list. Nevertheless, it is not true that each axiom implies all of its predecessors. The axiom (I) implies (0), and axiom (II) implies (I) [and therefore (0)]. This chain of implications breaks off at axiom (III), which implies neither (II), nor (I), nor (0). A topological space with at least two points and the trivial topology, for example, satisfies none of the first three separation axioms, but it does satisfy (III). In fact, the only closed set which does not contain every singleton in the space is the empty set $\emptyset$, and it and any singleton are separated by $\emptyset$ and the ground set S. The same example satisfies (IV), so likewise this axiom implies neither (II), (I), nor (0). Finally, axiom (IV) does not imply axiom (III). A counterexample in this case is $(S, \mathfrak{I})$, where $S = \{a, b\}$ and $\mathfrak{I} = \{\emptyset, \{a\}, S\}$. The only pairs of disjoint closed sets are $\{\emptyset, S\}$ and $\{\emptyset, \{b\}\}$, and they are both separated by $\emptyset$ and S, so the space satisfies (IV); but $\{a\}$ is a singleton not contained in the closed set $\{b\}$, whereas the only open set containing $\{b\}$, namely S, also contains $\{a\}$, so the space does not satisfy (III).

In a similar way, examples can be produced to show that none of the axioms in the list implies any of its successors (see the exercises). The matter can be summed up by saying that the only valid general implications between pairs of the separation axioms in the list are that (II) implies (I), (I) implies (0), and (II) implies (0).

The separation axiom (0) is sometimes called the Kolmogorov [Kolmogoroff] axiom, and a topological space that satisfies it is called a (T_0)-space, or a Kolmogorov space. Two simple statements equivalent to the axiom are: Of any two distinct singletons, at least one has the complement of the other as a neighborhood; the closures of two distinct singletons are distinct. This axiom is of relatively little importance.

Spaces satisfying (I) are called (T_1)-spaces. Some writers have insisted that all topological spaces should satisfy (I); for them, a topological space is a (T_1)-space by definition.

The following statement is numbered as a theorem not because it is particularly profound but because it is often cited.

THEOREM 18. A topological space $(S, \mathfrak{I})$ satisfies (I) if and only if every singleton in $(S, \mathfrak{I})$ (or, equivalently, every finite subset of S) is closed.

Proof. If $(S, \mathfrak{I})$ satisfies (I), and $x \in S$, then for every $y \in S - \{x\}$ there exists an open set U satisfying

$$y \in U \subset S - \{x\}.$$

Hence $S - \{x\}$ is a neighborhood of each of its points, and consequently (by Theorem 1) open; therefore $\{x\}$ is closed. Conversely, if every singleton in $(S, \mathfrak{I})$ is closed, and x and y are distinct elements of S, then $S - \{y\}$ is an open set to which x, but not y, belongs, so $(S, \mathfrak{I})$ satisfies (I). The part about finite subsets of S is provided for by (G_2) (p. 23).

The separation axiom (II) is nothing but Hausdorff's axiom (D) in disguise, so the topological spaces in which (II) is satisfied are essentially the topological spaces as Hausdorff defined them. For this reason, a topological space that satisfies (II) is often called—and is called in this book—a *Hausdorff space*. Alternative terms in wide use are (T_2)-*space* and *separated space*. Following Hausdorff's example, some mathematicians still reserve the term "topological space" for Hausdorff spaces.

Because Hausdorff spaces automatically satisfy axiom (I), it follows from Theorem 18 that singletons in Hausdorff spaces are always closed. Exercise 119 shows how this statement may be strengthened.

The separation axiom (III), sometimes called the Vietoris axiom, is seldom used alone. When it is satisfied, (I) and (II) imply each other. Axiom (II) implies (I) in any case, and if (I) holds, then singletons are closed according to Theorem 18, and (II) follows at once from (III). A topological space satisfying (III) and either (I) or (II)— hence all three—is called a (T_3)-*space*, or a *regular space*.

The situation for axiom (IV), sometimes called the Tietze separation axiom, is similar. It is seldom used alone, but spaces satisfying (IV) and either (I) or (II)—hence all three—is called a *normal space*, or a (T_4)-*space*. Normal spaces are regular, because when (I) is satisfied, (IV) implies (III).

A number of important special properties of topological spaces satisfying the various separation axioms are established intermittently throughout the rest of the book. In a general way, the separation axioms serve as guarantees that the topologies which satisfy them are fine enough for certain purposes; the topology in a (T_1)-space is fine enough to insulate any singleton from any other, the topology in a Hausdorff space is fine enough to separate singletons, and so on. The natural topology in a metric space is fine enough to do all these things:

THEOREM 19. A metrizable space satisfies all the separation axioms (0)–(IV).

Proof. Because of the relationships between the separation axioms that have already been pointed out, it will prove the theorem to show that every metrizable space satisfies (II) and (IV). Let $(S, 5)$ be any metrizable space, and let d be a metric on S such that $5_d = 5$. If x and y are distinct elements of S, then $d(x, y) = \alpha > 0$; hence $\{x\}$ and $\{y\}$ may be separated by the open balls $C(x, \alpha/2)$ and $C(y, \alpha/2)$—the disjointness of these two open balls follows by a simple indirect argument involving the triangle axiom. Thus (II). If F and G are disjoint closed sets and $x \in F$, then since G is closed and $x \notin G$, there must exist some positive number α_x such that $C(x, \alpha_x) \cap G = \emptyset$; that is, $d(x, y) \geq \alpha_x$ for every y belonging to G. Similarly, for every y belonging to G there exists a positive number β_y such that $d(x, y) \geq \beta_y$ for every $x \in F$. Then the sets

$$U = \cup \{C(x, \alpha_x/2) : x \in F\}$$

and

$$V = \cup \{C(y, \beta_y/2) : y \in G\}$$

are open supersets of F and G respectively. Moreover, $U \cap V = \emptyset$; for if $z \in U \cap V$, there must exist an x in F and a y in G for which

$$z \in C(x, \alpha_x/2) \cap C(y, \beta_y/2),$$

and then

$$d(x, y) \leq d(x, z) + d(y, z) < \alpha_x/2 + \beta_y/2 \leq \gamma,$$

where γ is the larger of the two numbers α_x and β_y; but this must contradict either $d(x, y) \geq \alpha_x$ or $d(x, y) \geq \beta_y$. This shows that U and V separate F and G, and completes the proof.

According to Theorem 19, the separation axioms (0)–(IV) collectively constitute a necessary condition (namely, normality) for the metrizability of a topological space. Unfortunately, this necessary condition is not sufficient.

Exercises

116. Show that if S is infinite and $\mathfrak{I}$ is the cofinite topology on S, then $(S, \mathfrak{I})$ satisfies (I) but not (II).

117. Find an example of a topological space that satisfies (0) but not (I).

118. Show that a topological space satisfies (III) if and only if it has the following property: If x is any point in the space, and $x \nmid N$, then there exists a closed subset of N which is also a neighborhood of x. Find a similar condition equivalent to (IV).

119. Show that a topological space satisfies (II) if and only if the singleton of any point x is the intersection of the collection of all closed neighborhoods of x.

120. Show that the topological product of any family of Hausdorff spaces is a Hausdorff space.

121. Prove that if f and g are continuous functions from the same topological space into the same Hausdorff space, then $\{x: f(x) = g(x)\}$ is closed.

Compactness. A subset of R^n is *bounded* if it is contained in some n-cell. Those subsets of R^n which are both closed and bounded have a number of properties that are extremely important in analysis. The two properties expressed by the following famous theorems are perhaps the most basic of these, because the others are usually derived from them.

THE HEINE-BOREL THEOREM. If M is a closed and bounded subset of R^n, and $\mathcal{O}$ is any collection of open subsets of R^n such that $M \subset \cup \mathcal{O}$, then there exists a finite subcollection $\mathcal{O}_1$ of $\mathcal{O}$ such that $M \subset \cup \mathcal{O}_1$.

THE BOLZANO-WEIERSTRASS THEOREM. If M is a closed and bounded subset of R^n, then any infinite subset of M has at least one cluster point in M.

Closed, bounded sets in R^n have so many admirable properties that it is natural to ask whether it might be possible to define a concept of "closed-and-boundedness" for sets in topological spaces in general in such a way that "closed-and-bounded" sets would continue to have most, if not all, of those properties.

The term "closed" already has a meaning in topological spaces, but the term "bounded" does not; moreover, unfortunately, there is no suitable way of defining "bounded" sets in topological spaces. (Even in R^1, boundedness is not a topological property: Any 1-cell, which is bounded, is homeomorphic to the whole of R^1, which is not.) This blocks any attempt to make a direct extension of the "closed-and-bounded" property to topological spaces.

A more devious, and more successful, approach to the problem is based on the observation that the crucial properties assigned to closed-and-bounded sets in R^n by the Heine-Borel and Bolzano-Weierstrass theorems *are* topological properties. It can also be shown (and is shown, a little later) that as far as subsets of R^n are concerned, the two properties are equivalent to each other, and to closed-and-boundedness itself. It is therefore natural to take one of the two properties to play the role of closed-and-boundedness for general topological spaces. Both routes have been followed, but the Heine-Borel property is now usually preferred. The term "compact" is used for sets with this property.

A few new terms will be helpful. If $(S, \Im)$ is a topological space, $X \subset S$, and Θ is a collection of subsets of S such that $X \subset \cup\Theta$, the collection Θ is called a *cover* of X. If also $\Theta \subset \Im$, Θ is called an *open cover* of X. In these terms, a set X in a topological space is *compact* if every open cover of X contains a finite cover of X.

This definition is not universally accepted. In fact, the terminology of compactness is disconcertingly chaotic. There are many different compactness-like concepts in circulation—two more are introduced in this chapter—and the word "compact," with or without prefixes or qualifying adverbs, is used for almost all of them. Whenever one encounters one of these terms, especially the word "compact" by itself, he should take some pains to discover just what is being meant by it.

The set X in the definition of compactness may be S itself; in this case the definition yields the concept of a *compact (topological) space*. It is a simple matter to show that a set X in $(S, \Im)$ is compact if and only if the associated subspace $(X, \Im_X)$ is a compact space.

In any topological space with a finite topology, every set is compact, for in such a space every open cover must itself be finite. In any topological space, then, every finite set is compact. An excellent case can be made for the claim that compactness serves as a generalization of finiteness.*

Another illustration of compactness is provided by the cofinite topological spaces introduced in Exercise 7, where S is any nonempty set and the open sets are the empty set and the complements of finite sets. Any subset X of S is compact in this space. Indeed, if Θ is any open cover of X, and $U \in \Theta$, then $X \cap \mathbf{C}U$ is finite. If this set is empty, then $\{U\}$ is already a finite cover of X contained in Θ. If it is not empty, then for each element x of $X \cap \mathbf{C}U$ there exists an element U_x of Θ such that $x \in U_x$, and the collection $\{U\} \cup \{U_x : x \in X \cap \mathbf{C}U\}$ is a cover of X which is finite and is contained in Θ.

Compactness can also be described by use of the so-called *finite intersection property* of collections. A nonempty collection of sets has this property if the intersection of every nonempty finite subcollection is nonempty. For example, in R^1 the collection of all sets of the form $\{x : x < a\}$, where a is a constant for each set, has the finite intersection property, even though the intersection of the whole collection is empty. The characterization of compactness in terms of this property is

* See E. Hewitt, "The Rôle of Compactness in Analysis," *American Mathematical Monthly*, **67**, 499–516 (1960).

THEOREM 20.   A topological space is compact if and only if the intersection of every collection of closed sets that has the finite
intersection property is nonempty.

This can be proved by straightforward indirect arguments based on
the De Morgan formulas.

It is a useful special consequence of Theorem 20 that if $(F_n : n \in Z^+)$
is a sequence of nonempty closed sets such that $F_n \supset F_{n+1}$ for all n,
and at least one set F_n is compact, then $\cap \{F_n : n \in Z^+\} \neq \emptyset$.

THEOREM 21.   Any closed set in a compact topological space is
compact.

In fact, if $(S, \mathfrak{I})$ is compact, and F is a closed subset of S, and $\mathcal{O}$ is an
open cover of F, then $\mathcal{O} \cup \{CF\}$ is an open cover of S, so there exists
a finite subcollection $\mathcal{O}_1$ of $\mathcal{O}$ such that $\mathcal{O}_1 \cup \{CF\}$ is an open cover of
S; but then $\mathcal{O}_1$ must be a cover of F.

Theorems 20 and 21 (and Exercise 124) are reminders of the intended
affinity between compactness and closedness.   Nevertheless, compact
sets are not necessarily closed.   For instance, finite sets, although
always compact, are not always closed.

Because of the way compactness is defined, it is preserved by
homeomorphisms; but a considerably weaker assumption about a
function is enough to guarantee that it preserves compactness.   The
next theorem gives the details.

THEOREM 22.   If $(S_1, \mathfrak{I}_1)$ and $(S_2, \mathfrak{I}_2)$ are topological spaces, $f : S_1 \to S_2$
is continuous, and X is a compact set in $(S_1, \mathfrak{I}_1)$, then $f(X)$ is
compact in $(S_2, \mathfrak{I}_2)$.

This theorem is sometimes expressed by saying that the continuous
image of a compact set is compact, or that continuity preserves
compactness.

Proof.   If $\mathfrak{U}$ is an open cover of $f(X)$, then

$$\mathcal{O} = \{f^{-1}(V) : V \in \mathfrak{U}\}$$

is a cover of X because of the set-theoretic properties of f^{-1}, and in
fact an open cover because f is continuous (Theorem 6).   Because
X is compact, there is a finite cover $\mathcal{O}_1$ of X contained in $\mathcal{O}$.   For
each $U \in \mathcal{O}_1$, let V be an element of $\mathfrak{U}$ such that $f^{-1}(V) = U$.   The
set of all such V is a finite subcollection $\mathfrak{U}_1$ of $\mathfrak{U}$, and

$$f(X) \subset f(\cup \mathcal{O}_1) \subset \cup \{f(U) : U \in \mathcal{O}_1\} \subset \cup \mathfrak{U}_1$$

(*Sets*, 27), so $f(X)$ is compact.

Exercises

122. Show that each of the following sets in R^1 is not compact. (*a*) The set of integers; (*b*) R^1 itself; (*c*) the interval $\{x: 0 < x < 1\}$; (*d*) the set of reciprocals of positive integers.

123. Show that the closure of the set (*d*) in Exercise 122 is compact.

124. Prove that the union of a finite collection of closed sets in a topological space is compact if and only if every set in the collection is compact.

Compactness in Hausdorff Spaces. The compact sets in a Hausdorff space always have certain desirable properties which compact sets in general may lack. Impressed by this fact, some contemporary writers on topology withhold the term "compact" unless the space concerned is a Hausdorff space. The next theorem provides a convenient starting point for an enumeration of some of these properties.

THEOREM 23. In a Hausdorff space, any two disjoint compact sets are separated.

Proof. If F and G are disjoint compact sets in a given Hausdorff space, and $x \in F$ while $y \in G$, there must exist, by the separation axiom (II), disjoint open sets $U(x, y)$ and $V(x, y)$ to which x and y respectively belong. For a fixed y, the collection $\{U(x, y): x \in F\}$ is an open cover of F. Therefore, because F is compact, there is a finite subset X_y of F such that

$$F \subset U(y) = \cup\{U(x, y): x \in X_y\}.$$

If such a set X_y is chosen for each y belonging to G, and $V(y)$ is defined as $\cap\{V(x, y): x \in X_y\}$, then the collection $\{V(y): y \in G\}$ is an open cover of G. Moreover,

$$U(y) \cap V(y) = \emptyset \quad \text{for} \quad \text{all points } y \text{ of } G. \tag{1}$$

Because G is compact, there is a finite subset Y of G such that $G \subset V = \cup\{V(y): y \in Y\}$. Now if U is taken to be the set $\cap\{U(y): y \in Y\}$, U is an open superset of F because it is the intersection of a finite collection of open supersets of F. Similarly, V is an open superset of G. Finally, it follows from (1) that $U \cap V = \emptyset$. Thus U and V separate F and G, as required.

The earlier remark that some compact sets are not closed does not apply in Hausdorff spaces.

THEOREM 24.   In a Hausdorff space, every compact set is closed.

Proof.   If F is a compact set in a Hausdorff space, and $x \notin F$, then $\{x\}$ and F are disjoint compact sets, and therefore separated, say by U_x and V_x.   Then the set $\cup\{U_x : x \notin F\}$ is open because it is the union of a collection of open sets; but it is also the complement of F, so F is closed.

THEOREM 25.   Every compact Hausdorff space is normal.

Proof.   If F and G are disjoint closed sets in a compact Hausdorff space, they are compact (Theorem 21) and therefore separated (Theorem 23).

THEOREM 26.   If $(S_1, \mathfrak{I}_1)$ is a compact space, $(S_2, \mathfrak{I}_2)$ is a Hausdorff space, and $f \colon S_1 \to S_2$ is one-to-one and continuous, then f is a homeomorphism.

Proof.   It must be shown that f^{-1} is continuous or, equivalently (Theorem 7) that the image of any closed set under f, which is $(f^{-1})^{-1}$, is closed.   Let F be any closed set in $(S_1, \mathfrak{I}_1)$; then F is compact (Theorem 21).   Therefore, $f(F)$ is compact (Theorem 22) and accordingly closed (Theorem 24).

Exercises
125. How could Theorem 24 be used to simplify the doing of Exercise 122?

126. To underscore the force of Theorem 26, construct an example of a function f from one compact space onto another which is continuous and one-to-one but not a homeomorphism.

The Tihonov Product Theorem.   If the compactness of a topological space is regarded as a kind of smallness, and the formation of topological products is thought of as a way of forming bigger topological spaces from given ones, it would seem plausible that the topological product of an infinite family of compact spaces might well fail to be compact.   In 1935, A. N. Tihonov [Tychonoff] published his famous "product theorem," which says in effect that this conjecture, however plausible, is false.

THEOREM 27.   The topological product of any family of compact topological spaces is compact.

Tihonov's proof and all its later variations and replacements use the controversial axiom of choice (*Sets*, 38–41) in some form.   This perhaps unfortunate circumstance is unavoidable for two reasons. First, the theorem itself would be meaningless, or at best poorly stated, in a mathematical system that had no axiom of choice. In order to make meaningful statements about "the topological product of any family of compact topological spaces" one should be able to assume that the Cartesian product of any family of nonempty sets is nonempty (the ground set of the topological product, as of any topological space, must be nonempty), and this assumption itself is a form of the axiom of choice! The difficulty could perhaps be avoided by inserting the phrase "if it exists" after the words "topological product" in the theorem. This, however, would not avoid the second difficulty, which is that Tihonov's theorem, even in this modified form, implies the axiom of choice.* In other words, since Tihonov's theorem and the axiom of choice may be derived from each other, the theorem is one of the many alternative forms of that protean axiom. The use of Tyhonov's theorem as a substitute for the more traditional forms of the axiom has not been seriously proposed, however; the traditional forms use simpler and less specialized terms and are therefore more directly useful in mathematics as a whole. For this reason there is some point in deriving Theorem 27 from one of the more fundamental forms of the axiom of choice instead of succumbing to the theoretically legitimate temptation to postulate it.

The following proof of Theorem 27 uses the axiom of choice in the form of "Zorn's lemma" (*Sets*, 41) and compactness as characterized by Theorem 20.

Let $((S_\alpha, \Im_\alpha): \alpha \in A)$ be a family of compact topological spaces, and let $(S, \Im)$ be the topological product of this family. Let $\Im$ be any collection of closed sets in $(S, \Im)$ with the finite intersection property. The goal is to show that $\cap \Im \neq \emptyset$.

Let $\mathbf{A}$ be the aggregate of all collections of subsets of S which have the finite intersection property and contain $\Im$. Any totally ordered subaggregate of $\mathbf{A}$ has an upper bound, namely its union, in $\mathbf{A}$. Therefore, according to Zorn's lemma, there exists a collection $\Im_1$ belonging to $\mathbf{A}$ with the property that if $\Im_1 \subset \Im_2$, where $\Im_2 \in \mathbf{A}$, then $\Im_1 = \Im_2$. The two following properties of $\Im_1$ will be needed shortly.

(1) The intersection of any finite subcollection of $\Im_1$ belongs to $\Im_1$.

(2) If $X \cap Y \neq \emptyset$ for all $Y \in \Im_1$, then $X \in \Im_1$.

---

* See J. L. Kelley, "The Tychonoff Product Theorem Implies the Axiom of Choice," *Fundamenta Mathematicae*, **37,** 75–76 (1950).

Statement (1) is true because if the intersection, say X, of some finite subcollection of $\mathcal{F}_1$ did not belong to $\mathcal{F}_1$, then $\mathcal{F}_1 \cup \{X\}$ would belong to A and would have $\mathcal{F}_1$ as a distinct subcollection, counter to the basic property of $\mathcal{F}_1$. Statement (2) is true for much the same reason.

If f_α is the projection from S onto S_α, then for each element α of A, $\{\overline{f_\alpha(X)} : X \in \mathcal{F}_1\}$ is a collection of closed sets in $(S_\alpha, \mathfrak{I}_\alpha)$ which has the finite intersection property. In fact, if $\mathfrak{K}$ is a finite subcollection of $\mathcal{F}_1$, then

$$\cap\{\overline{f_\alpha(X)} : X \in \mathfrak{K}\} \supset \overline{\cap\{f_\alpha(X) : X \in \mathfrak{K}\}}$$
$$\supset \cap\{f_\alpha(X) : X \in \mathfrak{K}\}$$
$$\supset f_\alpha(\cap\mathfrak{K}) \neq \emptyset,$$

because $\cap\mathfrak{K} \neq \emptyset$. [The successive inclusions here are based on Exercise 27, property (K_2) of closure, and *Sets*, 27.] Because of the compactness of $(S_\alpha, \mathfrak{I}_\alpha)$ then, $\cap\{\overline{f_\alpha(X)} : X \in \mathcal{F}_1\} \neq \emptyset$, and so by the axiom of choice (*Sets*, 39) there exists an $x = (x_\alpha : \alpha \in A)$ of S such that

$$x_\alpha \in \cap\{\overline{f_\alpha(X)} : X \in \mathcal{F}_1\}.$$

It will be shown that $x \in \cap\mathcal{F}$.

Let $x \prec N$. Then because of the definition of the product topology, there exists a finite subset A_1 of A such that $x \in U = \times_\alpha U_\alpha \subset N$, where $U_\alpha \in \mathfrak{I}_\alpha$, and $U_\alpha = S_\alpha$ if $\alpha \notin A_1$. For each $\alpha \in A_1$ and each $X \in \mathcal{F}_1$, $U_\alpha \cap f_\alpha(X) \neq \emptyset$, because $x_\alpha \in \overline{f_\alpha(X)}$. Therefore, $f_\alpha{}^{-1}(U_\alpha) \cap X \neq \emptyset$ for all X belonging to $\mathcal{F}_1$. This implies that $f_\alpha{}^{-1}(U_\alpha) \in \mathcal{F}_1$, by property (2) of $\mathcal{F}_1$; and then, by property (1),

$$U = \cap\{f_\alpha{}^{-1}(U_\alpha) : \alpha \in A_1\} \in \mathcal{F}_1.$$

Thus, if $X \in \mathcal{F}$, then $N \cap X \supset U \cap X \neq \emptyset$, because both U and X belong to $\mathcal{F}_1$, which has the finite intersection property. According to Theorem 5, $x \in \overline{X} = X$ for every X belonging to $\mathcal{F}$, so $x \in \cap\mathcal{F}$, as claimed. This ends the proof.

If "compact" is understood to mean "compact and Hausdorff," as sometimes happens, then Exercise 120 makes it possible to say that Theorem 27 remains true.

Exercises

127. Prove the converse of Theorem 27: If the topological product of a family of topological spaces is compact, then every space in the family is compact.

128. Prove that the Cantor ternary set is compact.

∗∗129. Prove directly, without appeal to Theorem 27 or to any form of the axiom of choice, that the product of two compact topological spaces is compact.

Sequences and Convergence. In order to provide the background for defining another kind of compactness, there must be a brief digression at this point. The subject of the digression is sequences in topological spaces. Here a sequence is denoted by a symbol of the form (x_n); this stands for the sequence $(x_n : n \in Z^+)$, as discussed in *Sets*, 32.

If $(S, \mathfrak{I})$ is a topological space, and (x_n) is a sequence in S, then (x_n) is said to *converge* to x ($x \in S$), or to have x as a *limit*, if for every neighborhood N of x, there exists an n_0 belonging to Z^+ such that $x_n \in N$ if $n \geq n_0$; or, equivalently, if $\{n \in Z^+ : x_n \notin N\}$ is finite. It follows immediately that a sequence (x_n) converges to x if and only if all of its subsequences converge to x.

For sequences in metric spaces, a straightforward adaptation of the familiar elementary definition of convergent sequences of real numbers gives a concept equivalent to the general one that has just been formulated. A sequence (x_n) in a metric space (S, d) converges to x if and only if the sequence $(d(x_n, x))$ converges to 0 in R^1.

In general topological spaces, sequences may converge without having a unique limit. For example—and it is the extreme example—in a trivial topological space any sequence converges to any point of the space. This unsavory situation cannot occur in a space that is well enough separated.

THEOREM 28. In a Hausdorff space, any sequence has at most one limit.

Proof. If $(S, \mathfrak{I})$ is a Hausdorff space and a sequence (x_n) in S converges to x and y, then, unless $x = y$, there exist disjoint sets U and V in $\mathfrak{I}$ that separate x and y. Since U and V are neighborhoods of x and y respectively, $\{n \in Z^+ : x_n \in U\}$ and $\{n \in Z^+ : x_n \in V\}$ are disjoint subsets of Z^+ each of which has a finite complement; but this is impossible, so it must be that $x = y$.

Exercises

130. Which sequences in a discrete topological space converge?

131. Show that in any topological space the set of limits of any given sequence is closed.

132. Suppose that there is given an abstract concept of convergence for sequences in some nonempty set S; that is, to certain sequences (x_n) in S there are assigned "limits" in a perfectly arbitrary way. A subset X of S may then be called *convergence-open* if it has the property that whenever a sequence (x_n) has a limit x belonging to X, then $\{n \in Z^+ : x_n \notin X\}$ is finite. Show that the collection of all convergence-open subsets of S is a topology on S. What prevents this from being a satisfactory construction?

Sequential and Fréchet Compactness. Experience has shown that it is often convenient, and not always unreasonable, to stipulate that every sequence in some topological space has a convergent subsequence. (It is normally unreasonable to assume that every sequence converges!) More generally, a set in a topological space may have this property; one says that a set X in a topological space is *sequentially compact* if every sequence in X has a subsequence converging to a limit that belongs to X.

If the range of a sequence is infinite, limits of subsequences tend to be cluster points of the range—the exact situation is examined later. This phenomenon suggests that there might be some point in looking at the property: Any infinite subset of X has at least one cluster point in X. At the cost of some historical accuracy, this property will be called *Fréchet compactness*. In the older literature, and in some that is not so old, this property is sometimes called just compactness; those who adopt this usage usually employ the term "bicompactness" for the property called compactness in the preceding sections. Fréchet compactness is precisely the property assigned to closed, bounded subsets of R^n by the Bolzano-Weierstrass theorem. Fréchet compactness is often also called *countable compactness*.

Nonelementary examples can be constructed to show that no two of the three concepts of compactness that have now been introduced are equivalent in topological spaces in general. In fact, the following theorem says all that can be said about the relationships between the three kinds of compactness without making special assumptions.

THEOREM 29. Either compactness or sequential compactness implies Fréchet compactness.

Proof. Since a set in a topological space has one of the three compactness properties if and only if the corresponding subspace has that property, it is fair to assume that the theorem refers to some space as a whole and to prove it on those terms. If $(S, \mathfrak{I})$ is a space which is

Separation, Compactness, and Connectedness · **83**

not Fréchet compact, there exists an infinite subset X of S which has no cluster point. Because it has no cluster point, X is closed. Moreover, for each point x of X one can choose a neighborhood U_x, which can be assumed to be open, such that $U_x \cap (X - \{x\}) = \emptyset$. The collection

$$\{\mathsf{C}X\} \cup \{U_x : x \in X\}$$

is then an open cover of S which contains no finite cover: Remove even one of the infinitely many sets U_x and the collection is no longer a cover of S. Thus the space is not compact. This shows that compactness implies Fréchet compactness. Now if $(S, \mathcal{I})$ is sequentially compact, and X is an infinite subset of S, one can form a sequence in X by taking x_1 to be any point of X, x_2 to be any point of $X - \{x_1\}$, x_3 to be any point of $X - \{x_1, x_2\}$, and so on.* The sequence (x_n) will have the special property that $x_m \neq x_n$ if $m \neq n$. Because of the assumed sequential compactness, this sequence has a convergent subsequence. If y is a limit of such a subsequence and $y \prec N$, then $x_n \in N$ for infinitely many n, and

$$N \cap (X - \{y\}) \neq \emptyset,$$

because the intersection contains all of the points x_n which belong to N with at most the one exception y. The point y is therefore a cluster point of X. This completes the proof.

Exercises

133. Show that a closed subset of a sequentially compact space is sequentially compact.

134. Prove Theorem 22 with "Fréchet compact" in place of "compact."

∗**135.** Show that a Hausdorff space is sequentially compact if and only if every closed subset for which the relative topology is discrete is finite.

∗**136.** Show that if (F_n) is a sequence of nonempty closed sets satisfying $F_n \supset F_{n+1}$ (for all n) in a Fréchet compact (T_1)-space, then $\cap \{F_n : n \in Z^+\} \neq \emptyset$.

Compactness in Metric Spaces. The relationship between the three kinds of compactness becomes much simpler when the spaces

---

* The general idea of this construction, which is described rather loosely here, will be used several times in the next few pages. For a careful discussion of the principle involved, see P. R. Halmos, *Naive Set Theory*, D. Van Nostrand Company, Princeton, 1960, pp. 60–61.

concerned are metric spaces, because for such spaces the three are entirely equivalent. Most of this section is devoted to proving this important fact.

First, a Fréchet compact metric space is sequentially compact. Let (S, d) be a Fréchet compact metric space, and let (x_n) be any sequence in S. If the range of (x_n) is finite, then there is some point x in S such that $x_n = x$ for infinitely many n; and the terms x_n for which this equation holds can be regarded in a natural way as the terms of a subsequence of (x_n); this subsequence clearly converges to x. If, on the other hand, the range of (x_n) is infinite, it has a cluster point x. In this case the neighborhood $U_1 = C(x, 1)$ contains at least one point x_n different from x, say x_{n_1}. Then the neighborhood $U_2 = C(x, \alpha_2)$, where α_2 is the smallest of the positive numbers $\frac{1}{2}$, $d(x, x_1)$, . . . , $d(x, x_{n_1})$, must contain a term of (x_n) different from x; let this be x_{n_2}. Necessarily, $n_2 > n_1$. Then if α_3 is the smallest number among $\frac{1}{3}$, $d(x, x_1)$, . . . , $d(x, x_{n_2})$, the neighborhood $C(x, \alpha_3)$ of x contains a point x_{n_3} which is different from x, and $n_3 > n_2$—and so on. The subsequence (x_{n_k}) of (x_n) constructed in this way converges to x. Thus any sequence (x_n) has a convergent subsequence, so the space (S, d) is sequentially compact.

In view of Theorem 29, then, sequential compactness and Fréchet compactness are equivalent for metric spaces.

The missing link in the chain of implications will be supplied by showing that a sequentially compact metric space is compact. This is a somewhat taller order, and justifies the introduction of an auxiliary concept: A metric space (S, d) is *totally bounded* if, for every positive real number ϵ, there exists a finite subset X of S such that

$$\{C(x, \epsilon): x \in X\}$$

is a cover of S.

The first step is to prove that *a sequentially compact metric space is totally bounded*. In fact, suppose that for some metric space (S, d) and some positive number ϵ there is no finite set X of the kind required for total boundedness. Let $x_1 \in S$. Since $\{C(x_1, \epsilon)\}$ is not a cover of S, there exists a point x_2 belonging to $\mathsf{C}[C(x_1, \epsilon)]$. Then since $\{C(x_1, \epsilon), C(x_2, \epsilon)\}$ is not a cover of S, there exists a point x_3 belonging to

$$\mathsf{C}[C(x_1, \epsilon) \cup C(x_2, \epsilon)]$$

—and so on. In this way one can define a sequence (x_n) in S such that $d(x_r, x_s) \geq \epsilon$ if $r \neq s$. No subsequence of (x_n) can converge, because if x is any point of S, it follows from the triangle inequality that $x_n \in C(x, \epsilon/2)$ for at most one value of n. This proves the italicized statement.

The next step is to prove the somewhat startling statement that *if $\mathfrak{U}$ is any open cover of a sequentially compact metric space, there exists a number $\epsilon > 0$ such that every open ball of radius ϵ is contained in some member of $\mathfrak{U}$.* Again, an indirect proof is in order. If the conclusion is false, then for each positive integer n there exists a point x_n of S such that $C(x_n, 1/n)$ is not contained in any member of $\mathfrak{U}$. Some subsequence of the sequence (x_n) has a limit x, which must belong to some member of $\mathfrak{U}$, say U. Because the open balls centered at points and with radii of the form $1/n$ form a fundamental system of neighborhoods (Theorem 17), $C(x, 1/p) \subset U$ for some positive integer p. The point x is a limit of a subsequence of (x_n), so $x_n \in C(x, 1/2p)$ for at least one n satisfying $n > 2p$. But the triangle inequality can now be used to show that for such an n,

$$C(x_n, 1/n) \subset C(x, 1/p) \subset U;$$

and this contradicts the original assumption about the sequence (x_n).

With the equipment just developed it is easy to show that a sequentially compact metric space is compact. If (S, d) is a sequentially compact metric space with a given open cover $\mathfrak{U}$, then by the last fact proved there exists a positive number ϵ such that every open ball of radius ϵ is contained in some member of $\mathfrak{U}$. For a fixed ϵ with this property, there exists a finite set X such that

$$\{C(x, \epsilon) : x \in X\}$$

is a cover of S, since (S, d) is totally bounded. For each $x \in X$, let U_x be a member of $\mathfrak{U}$ containing $C(x, \epsilon)$. Then $\mathfrak{U}_1 = \{U_x : x \in X\}$ is a finite subcollection of $\mathfrak{U}$, and it is a cover of S. Thus (S, d) is compact.

This completes the proof of

THEOREM 30. For metrizable spaces, the properties of compactness, Fréchet compactness, and sequential compactness are equivalent to one another.

A simple necessary condition for the compactness (sequential compactness, Fréchet compactness) of a set in a metric space is provided by the next theorem, the proof of which is left as an exercise.

THEOREM 31. In a metric space, a compact set is closed and bounded.

(Recall that a set X in a metric space is bounded if there exists a positive number M such that $d(x, y) \leq M$ for all points x and y belonging to X; or, alternatively, if X is contained in some open ball.)

The condition in Theorem 31 is not sufficient for compactness, however; if a metric space is defined as in Example 2, p. 68, where S is infinite, then the whole space is bounded and of course closed, but is not compact:

$$\{C(x, \alpha/2) : x \in S\}$$

is an open cover of S containing no finite cover (nor, indeed, any cover but itself).

This section concludes with a theorem of a different kind, which is useful in many applications. It is concerned with the concept of the distance between sets in a metric space. If (S, d) is a metric space, and X and Y are nonempty subsets of S, the *distance* $\delta_d(X, Y)$ between X and Y is defined by

$$\delta_d(X, Y) = \inf \{d(x, y) : x \in X \text{ and } y \in Y\}.$$

This quantity always exists as a non-negative real number, but δ_d cannot normally be regarded as a metric on $\mathcal{P}(S)$, or even on $\mathcal{P}(S) - \{\emptyset\}$, because it satisfies neither (M$_1$) nor (M$_3$). Nevertheless, δ_d is useful in various ways. For example, the closure of a nonempty set X in a metric space (S, d) can be described as $\{x : \delta_d(\{x\}, X) = 0\}$; this can be quickly proved by use of Theorem 12.

Clearly, if $X \cap Y \neq \emptyset$, then $\delta_d(X, Y) = 0$. The converse of this statement is not generally true. For instance, if in R^2 the set X is taken to be the hyperbola $\{(x, y) : xy = 1\}$ and Y is taken to be the line $\{(x, y) : x = 0\}$, then $\delta_d(X, Y) = 0$, but $X \cap Y = \emptyset$. This happens even though X and Y are both closed sets.

When compactness enters, the situation becomes simpler.

THEOREM 32.   If X and Y are disjoint, nonempty, compact sets in a metric space (S, d), then $\delta_d(X, Y) > 0$; and there exist points $x \in X$ and $y \in Y$ such that $d(x, y) = \delta_d(X, Y)$.

The theorem is best proved by taking the second part first. By the definition of δ_d, there exist sequences (x_n) and (y_n) in X and Y respectively such that the sequence $(d(x_n, y_n))$ converges to $\delta_d(X, Y)$ in R^1 (*Sets*, 47). Since X is sequentially compact, the sequence (x_n) has a convergent subsequence, say (x_{n_k}); let its limit be x, which belongs to X. Then the sequence (y_{n_k}) has a convergent subsequence $(y_{n_{k_i}})$ with a limit y belonging to Y. If (to clean up the notation) a_i is defined to be $x_{n_{k_i}}$ and b_i is taken to be $y_{n_{k_i}}$, then the sequence (a_i), as a subsequence of (x_{n_k}), converges to x; and (b_i) converges to y by construction. From these facts and the triangle inequality it follows that the sequence $(d(a_i, b_i))$ converges to $d(x, y)$. At the same time, however, $(d(a_i, b_i))$ is a subsequence of $(d(x_n, y_n))$ and therefore converges to $\delta_d(X, Y)$. By Theorems 19 and 28, a sequence in a metric space cannot have two different limits; therefore $d(x, y) = \delta_d(X, Y)$, and this disposes of the latter part of the theorem. The former part is a consequence of this and (M_1), since certainly $x \neq y$.

Exercises

137. Prove Theorem 31.

138. Let (S, d) be a metric space. Using δ_d, show that for any compact set X in this space there exists a continuous function $f: S \to R^1$ such that $\{x \in S : f(x) = 0\} = X$.

*__139.__ Prove the first part of Theorem 32 by direct use of the fundamental notion of compactness, not sequential compactness.

Compact Sets in Euclidean Spaces. According to Example 1, p. 68, n-dimensional Euclidean space can be regarded, in a very direct way, as a metric space. It is of far more than mere historical interest to determine exactly which sets in a metric space of this particular class are compact. Theorem 31 says that in any metric space compact sets are closed and bounded. The goal of this section is to show that in Euclidean spaces, conversely, every closed and bounded set is compact. In short, the Heine-Borel theorem (and therefore, because of Theorem 30, the Bolzano-Weierstrass theorem too) will be proved.

The starting point will be one form of the classical one-dimensional Bolzano-Weierstrass theorem: *In R^1, any set of the form*

$$[a, b] = \{x : a \leq x \leq b\}$$

is sequentially compact. It will be assumed for convenience that $a = 0$ and $b = 1$. This does not really reduce the generality of the proof, because any nonempty $[a, b]$ is homeomorphic to $[0, 1]$. Let (x_n) be any sequence in $[0, 1]$. For at least one of the sets $[0, \frac{1}{2}]$ and $[\frac{1}{2}, 1]$ it must be true that x_n belongs to that set for infinitely many n; call one for which this is true I_1. Then, similarly, divide I_1 into two pieces "of equal length" and call I_2 a piece to which infinitely many terms of (x_n) belong. The result of continuing this process indefinitely is a sequence (I_k) of subsets of $[0, 1]$ with the properties: (i) $I_k \supset I_{k+1}$ for all k; (ii) if x and y both belong to I_k, $d(x, y) = |x - y| \leq 2^{-k}$; (iii) for each k, $x_n \in I_k$ for infinitely many n. One can then form a subsequence (x_{n_k}) of (x_n) by choosing $x_{n_1} \in I_1$, $x_{n_2} \in I_2$ with $n_2 > n_1$, $x_{n_3} \in I_3$ with $n_3 > n_2$, and so on. If m and s are any positive integers, and $r > m$, it follows from (i) and (ii) that $\left| x_{n_{r+s}} - x_{n_r} \right| < 2^{-m}$. Thus the subsequence (x_{n_k}) satisfies the requirements of the Cauchy convergence principle (*Sets*, 48, 49), and must therefore have a limit x. Because $[0, 1]$ is closed, $x \in [0, 1]$. This shows that every sequence in $[0, 1]$ has a subsequence with a limit in this set; that is, $[0, 1]$ is sequentially compact, and therefore compact in both of the other senses.

Now let X be any closed, bounded set in R^n. Because it is bounded, there exists a positive real number β such that $X \subset C(a, \beta)$ for some point a. But from the definition of the metric,

$$X \subset \overline{C(a, \beta)} \subset \{x \colon \left| x_k - a_k \right| \leq \beta \text{ for } k = 1, \ldots, n\}.$$

The subspace of R^n whose ground set appears on the right side here can be viewed as the topological product of the family of subspaces of R^1 which may be written, in terms of the respective ground sets, as

$$\{[a_k - \beta, a_k + \beta] \colon k = 1, \ldots, n\},$$

and is therefore compact by the restricted Bolzano-Weierstrass theorem just proved, and Theorem 27. As a closed subset of this compact set, X itself is compact according to Theorem 21. The next theorem sums it up.

THEOREM 33. In R^n, a set is compact if and only if it is both closed and bounded.

One special consequence of Theorem 33 is that any compact set in R^1 has a largest and a smallest element. As a bounded set, it has both a supremum and an infimum, and both must belong to the set because it is closed.

THEOREM 34. If $(S, \mathfrak{I})$ is a compact topological space, and $f \colon S \to R^1$ is continuous, then f attains an absolute maximum and an absolute minimum; that is, $f(S)$ has a largest and a smallest element.

In fact, according to Theorem 22, $f(S)$ is a compact subset of R^1, so the conclusion follows from the remark that precedes the theorem.

Because of the enormous interest of maxima and minima in many parts of both pure and applied mathematics, Theorem 34, which also is usually attributed to Weierstrass, is in constant use. This may be an adequate excuse for giving a second proof, which does not depend on Theorem 33.

Under the conditions stated in the theorem, if

$$J_n = \{y \in R^1 \colon |y| < n\} \qquad (n \in Z^+),$$

then $\{f^{-1}(J_n)\colon n \in Z^+\}$ is an open cover of S, and there consequently exists a finite subset Z_1 of Z^+ such that $\{f^{-1}(J_n)\colon n \in Z_1\}$ itself is a cover of S. If n_1 is the largest element of Z_1, then $S \subset f^{-1}(J_{n_1})$; that is $f(S) \subset J_{n_1}$. Thus every continuous function from S to R^1 is bounded in this sense, which is the usual one for real-valued functions. If there were such a function with the property that the supremum r of $f(S)$ did not belong to $f(S)$—that is, if f did not attain an absolute maximum—then the function $f_1\colon S \to R^1$ defined by the formula $f_1(x) = (r - f(x))^{-1}$ would be a continuous but unbounded function from S to R^1, and this is impossible. The assumption that f has no absolute minimum leads to a similar contradiction.

Exercises

140. Show that if $(S, \mathfrak{I})$ is a compact space, and $f\colon S \to R^1$ is a continuous function with the property that $f(x) > 0$ for every x in S, then there exists a positive number ϵ such that $f(x) > \epsilon$ for every x.

141. Draw up a proof of Theorem 32 that does not use sequences, but uses Theorem 27, Theorem 34, and the fundamental properties of a metric.

The One-Point Compactification. Not every topological space is compact, but it is possible to bring noncompact spaces within reach of some advantages of compactness by the device called *compactification*. In its simplest form, compactification is done by adjoining one or more points to the given ground set and defining a topology on the enlarged set in such a way that (i) the new topological space is compact and (ii) the original space is a subspace of the new one. More generally, one constructs a compact topological space that has a subspace homeomorphic to the given space.

One method of compactification—others are not considered in this book—is the *one-point*, or *Aleksandrov compactification*. Let $(S, \mathfrak{I})$ be a given topological space, and let x_∞ be any object that is not an element of S; it is taken for granted here that such an object always exists. Form the set $S_1 = S \cup \{x_\infty\}$, and define a collection $\mathfrak{I}_1$ by saying that a subset X of S_1 shall belong to $\mathfrak{I}_1$ if either (i) $X \in \mathfrak{I}$ or (ii) $\mathbf{C}X$ (the complement is with respect to S_1) is a closed and compact set in $(S, \mathfrak{I})$. This $\mathfrak{I}_1$ is a topology; the topological space $(S_1, \mathfrak{I}_1)$ is compact; and $(S, \mathfrak{I})$ is a subspace of $(S_1, \mathfrak{I}_1)$. The verification of these and other properties of the one-point compactification is left to the exercises.

EXAMPLE. Let $(S, \mathfrak{I})$ be the Euclidean line R^1. Because of Theorem 33, the sets of $\mathfrak{I}_1$ are those of $\mathfrak{I}$ along with those of the form $U \cup \{x_\infty\}$, where U is a subset of R^1 whose complement is closed and bounded. The compactification $(S_1, \mathfrak{I}_1)$ is homeomorphic to the unit circle C (p. 58). In fact, the function $f\colon S_1 \to C$ defined by

$$f(x) = \left(\frac{1 - x^2}{1 + x^2}, \frac{2x}{1 + x^2}\right) \quad \text{if} \quad x \in S$$

and

$$f(x_\infty) = (-1, 0)$$

is a homeomorphism between the two spaces. The proof of this, too, is left as an exercise.

Exercises

142. In terms of the preceding discussion, show that $\mathfrak{I}_1$ is a topology.

143. Show that $(S_1, \mathfrak{I}_1)$ is compact.

144. Show that $\mathfrak{I}$ is the relative topology on S in $(S_1, \mathfrak{I}_1)$.

145. Show that S is dense in $(S_1, \mathfrak{I}_1)$ if and only if $(S, \mathfrak{I})$ is not compact.

146. A topological space is *locally compact* if every point has a compact neighborhood. Show that $(S_1, \mathfrak{I}_1)$ is a Hausdorff space if and only if $(S, \mathfrak{I})$ is a locally compact Hausdorff space.

147. Prove that the function f in the example is a homeomorphism.

Connectedness. "Connected," like "compact," is too appropriate and suggestive a word to have been permitted to have only one meaning in topology. It appears frequently in the literature, with or without modifying adverbs, covering an impressive range of different concepts. The particular sense in which it is used here is exceptionally simple and useful. Another type of connectedness is considered briefly at the end of the chapter.

The goal is to formalize the more or less intuitive idea expressed by saying that a topological space is "in one coherent piece." It will help to look at the opposite idea, that of a space being composed of at least two pieces which do not cohere. It will simplify matters (without sacrifice, as events will prove) to consider the case in which there are exactly two pieces, say X and Y. To say that the whole space is composed of these pieces seems to imply that neither X nor Y

should be empty, that $X \cup Y = S$, and that $X \cap Y = \emptyset$. But there is more: one wants these sets not to "cohere." One way of getting at this somewhat vague idea without using nontopological terms is to say that there are not points of X arbitrarily close to Y, and there are not points of Y arbitrarily close to X. In more formal terms, if $x \in X$ for x arbitrarily close to x_0 ($x_0 \in S$), then $x_0 \notin Y$; and the same with X and Y interchanged. According to the interpretive schemes of Chapter 2, this becomes

$$\overline{X} \subset \mathbf{C}Y \quad \text{and} \quad \overline{Y} \subset \mathbf{C}X.$$

Because $X = \mathbf{C}Y$, the final conclusion is that X and Y are both closed or, equivalently, both open. In summary, a natural interpretation of the statement that a space is composed of two pieces which do not cohere to each other seems to be that the ground set of the space can be expressed as the union of two disjoint nonempty open sets. This sets the stage for the following definitions.

A partition of the ground set of a topological space which consists of two nonempty open sets will be called a *disconnecting partition* of the space. A topological space is *connected* if there exists no disconnecting partition of the space, *disconnected* if a disconnecting partition exists. The "open" here could be replaced by "closed," for each set in the partition must be the complement of the other. Equivalently, one can say that a topological space is connected if the only sets in it which are both open and closed are the empty set and the ground set.

There is nothing to be gained by allowing a disconnecting partition to consist of more than two sets. One might well say that a disconnecting partition of $(S, \mathfrak{I})$ is any partition of S consisting of *at least two* open sets. If $\mathfrak{Q}$ were such a partition, then by choosing X at random in $\mathfrak{Q}$ and then putting $Y = \cup(\mathfrak{Q} - \{X\})$, one would get a two-set disconnecting partition $\{X, Y\}$, and one would have to conclude that the space is disconnected in the sense defined in the preceding paragraph.

A nonempty set X in a given topological space is said to be connected if the corresponding subspace is a connected topological space; and the empty set is a connected set by general consent. In view of the definition of the relative topology, one can therefore say that a set X in the topological space $(S, \mathfrak{I})$ is connected if and only if there do not exist sets U and V belonging to $\mathfrak{I}$ such that

$$X \subset U \cup V, \quad X \cap U \neq \emptyset, \quad X \cap V \neq \emptyset,$$

but

$$X \cap U \cap V = \emptyset.$$

It is not safe to omit the X from the last of these conditions. For example, in the topological space whose ground set is $S = \{a, b, c\}$ and whose topology is $\{\emptyset, \{a\}, \{a, b\}, \{a, c\}, S\}$, the set $X = \{b, c\}$ has the unique disconnecting partition obtained by taking $U = \{a, b\}$ and $V = \{a, c\}$, but $U \cap V = \{a\} \neq \emptyset$.

The definition of connectedness is a negative one, and for this reason proofs of theorems about connectedness tend naturally to be indirect proofs. This appears repeatedly in the proofs that follow.

THEOREM 35. If X is a connected set, and $X \subset Y \subset \overline{X}$, then Y is connected.

In particular, then, the closure of any connected set is connected.

Proof. Suppose that $X \subset Y \subset \overline{X}$. If $X = \emptyset$, then $\overline{X} = \emptyset$ and so also $Y = \emptyset$; and the empty set being connected by decree, there is nothing to prove. If $X \neq \emptyset$ and Y is disconnected, then X is disconnected. Indeed, if U and V are open sets that make $\{Y \cap U, Y \cap V\}$ a disconnecting partition of Y, then it is easy to see that $X \cap U$ and $X \cap V$ are open relative to X and disjoint, and that their union is X. If $X \cap U$ were empty, and if $x \in Y \cap U$, U would be a neighborhood of x disjoint from X, and this would contradict the fact that x is a cluster point of X:

$$x \in Y - X \subset \overline{X} - X \subset X'.$$

Thus $X \cap U \neq \emptyset$, and in exactly the same way one can show that $X \cap V \neq \emptyset$. This shows that $\{X \cap U, X \cap V\}$ is a disconnecting partition of X, so X is not connected.

THEOREM 36. If the intersection of each pair of sets in a collection of connected sets is not empty, the union of the collection is connected.

Proof. If $\mathcal{Q}$ is the collection, and $A = \cup \mathcal{Q}$, suppose that A has a disconnecting partition $\{A \cap U, A \cap V\}$, where U and V are open sets in the given space. Since $A \cap U \neq \emptyset$ and $A \cap V \neq \emptyset$, there must exist sets X and Y belonging to $\mathcal{Q}$ and satisfying $X \cap U \neq \emptyset$ and $Y \cap V \neq \emptyset$. Then by assumption there exists an x belonging to $X \cap Y$. If $x \in A \cap U$, then $x \in Y \cap U$, so Y has the disconnecting partition $\{Y \cap U, Y \cap V\}$. If $x \notin A \cap U$, then $x \in A \cap V$ and similarly $\{X \cap U, X \cap V\}$ is a disconnecting partition of X. In either case, the assumption that $\mathcal{Q}$ consists of connected sets is contradicted. (See the figure on p. 94.)

Separation, Compactness, and Connectedness · 93

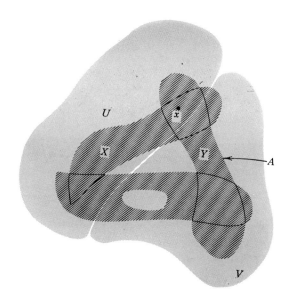

The concept of connectedness leads to a natural way of partitioning the ground set of any given topological space into connected subsets. If x is any point in such a space, and $\mathfrak{K}(x)$ is the collection of all connected sets to which x belongs—this collection is never empty, because $\{x\}$ belongs to it—then according to Theorem 36 the set K_x, defined to be the union of $\mathfrak{K}(x)$, is connected. It is called the (connected) *component* of x. The collection of all components in a given space is a partition of the ground set. It is easy to see that components are not empty, and that they form a cover of the space. If two components are not disjoint, say $K_x \cap K_y \neq \emptyset$, then Theorem 36 says that $K_x \cup K_y$ is connected, and since it has both x and y as elements, $K_x \cup K_y \subset K_x$ and $K_x \cup K_y \subset K_y$; and from these inclusions it follows that $K_x = K_y$.

The component of a point can be described, with the usual interpretation of the word "largest," as the largest connected set to which that point belongs; and a space is clearly connected if and only if it has only one component—that is, if any two points in it have the same component. One general property of components is that they are always closed: According to Theorem 35, if K_x is any component, then $\overline{K}_x$ is a connected set, so $\overline{K}_x \subset K_x$.

It might be expected that if K is a component of a disconnected topological space $(S, \mathfrak{I})$, the pair $\{K, \mathbf{C}K\}$ should be a disconnecting partition of the space. This is not necessarily so, because components may fail to be open. The Cantor ternary set T, playing its usual role as the versatile counter-example, provides an illustration. According to Exercise 152, the component of any point in this set (regarded, with its relative topology, as a topological space) is the singleton of the point. The Cantor set is compact (Exercise 128, p. 82) and clearly infinite. Therefore, according to Exercise 151, some component of T must be nonopen. Indeed, it can be shown directly that every component of T is nonopen.

Exercises

148. Which discrete topological spaces are connected? which cofinite topological spaces?

149. Prove that each of the following statements is equivalent to the statement that $(S, \mathfrak{I})$ is disconnected. (*a*) There exists a partition of S consisting of two separated nonempty sets. (*b*) There are at least four distinct subsets of S with empty boundaries.

150. Show that if each pair of points in a topological space $(S, \mathfrak{I})$ is contained in some connected subset of S, the whole space is connected.

151. Show that the collection of components of a compact space is finite if and only if every component is open.

152. A topological space is *totally disconnected* if the component of each point x is $\{x\}$. Prove that the Cantor ternary set is totally disconnected.

Connectedness and Continuity. By the very way in which it is defined, connectedness is preserved by homeomorphisms. Like compactness, however, the property of connectedness is preserved by functions that are merely continuous. This important fact is restated in the next theorem.

THEOREM 37. If $(S_1, \mathfrak{I}_1)$ and $(S_2, \mathfrak{I}_2)$ are topological spaces, $(S_1, \mathfrak{I}_1)$ is connected, and $f: S_1 \rightarrow S_2$ is continuous, then $f(S_1)$ is a connected set in $(S_2, \mathfrak{I}_2)$.

In particular, if all the conditions of Theorem 37 are met and f is also onto, then $(S_2, \mathfrak{I}_2)$ is connected. There is a simple indirect proof of the theorem which consists in showing that if $\{f(S_1) \cap U_2, f(S_1) \cap V_2\}$, where U_2 and V_2 belong to $\mathfrak{I}_2$, is a disconnecting partition of $f(S_1)$, then $\{f^{-1}(U_2), f^{-1}(V_2)\}$ is a disconnecting partition of $(S_1, \mathfrak{I}_1)$.

Theorem 37 has a number of direct general consequences which need not be listed here as theorems, but which are certainly worth mentioning. One is that if the topological product of some family of topological spaces is connected, then every space in that family must be connected. To prove this statement all one has to do is to apply Theorem 37 with the product space as $(S_1, \mathfrak{I}_1)$, the space in question as $(S_2, \mathfrak{I}_2)$, and the associated projection as f. The converse statement, although also true, is not so easy to prove and is not proved here. If $(S, \mathfrak{I})$ is a connected topological space and E is any equivalence relation on S, the quotient space $(S/E, \mathfrak{I}_E)$ is connected; for the natural mapping is a continuous function from one space onto the other.

The next theorem is perhaps of secondary interest, but it is helpful in constructing remarkable examples of connected sets and in various other ways. It will perhaps make better sense after a few preliminary remarks. If $(S_1, \mathfrak{I}_1)$ and $(S_2, \mathfrak{I}_2)$ are topological spaces, and $f: S_1 \to S_2$, then, since f is primarily a subset of $S_1 \times S_2$, one can study that subspace of the topological product of the two given spaces whose ground set is f. It would not be too far from traditional connotations to call this space $(f, \mathfrak{I}_f)$ the graph of f. As a topological space, $(f, \mathfrak{I}_f)$ may be nominated for various topological distinctions—for instance, that of connectedness.

THEOREM 38. Under the circumstances just described, if f is continuous and $(S_1, \mathfrak{I}_1)$ is connected, then $(f, \mathfrak{I}_f)$ is also connected.

In other words, the graph of a continuous function is connected if its domain is connected. This follows from Theorem 37 and the very general statement that *when f is continuous, $(f, \mathfrak{I}_f)$ is homeomorphic to* $(S_1, \mathfrak{I}_1)$. This statement may be proved by showing that the function $\varphi: S_1 \to f$ defined by

$$\varphi(x) = (x, f(x)) \qquad (x \in S_1)$$

is a homeomorphism. It is certainly one-to-one and onto. According to Theorem 15(iv) and the definition of product topologies, the collection

$$\{f \cap (U_1 \times U_2) : U_1 \in \mathfrak{I}_1 \text{ and } U_2 \in \mathfrak{I}_2\}$$

is a base for $\mathfrak{I}_f$. Now

$$\varphi^{-1}[f \cap (U_1 \times U_2)] = U_1 \cap f^{-1}(U_2).$$

Since f is continuous, $f^{-1}(U_2) \in \mathfrak{I}_1$; hence

$$\varphi^{-1}[f \cap (U_1 \times U_2)] \in \mathfrak{I}_1.$$

It follows easily from this that φ is continuous. At the same time, if $U_1 \in \mathfrak{I}_1$, then

$$\varphi(U_1) = \{(x, f(x)) : x \in U_1\} = f \cap (U_1 \times S_2) \in \mathfrak{I}_f,$$

so φ^{-1} is also continuous.

Exercise
153. Show that a topological space $(S_1, \mathfrak{I}_1)$ is disconnected if and only if there exists a continuous function from S_1 onto S_2, where $(S_2, \mathfrak{I}_2)$ is a couple (p. 59).

Connectedness in Euclidean Spaces. As with compactness, there is a good deal of value in trying to see just which sets in R^1, if not in higher-dimensional Euclidean spaces, are connected. For R^1 itself, there is again a simple criterion. It will involve the concept of order-convexity; a subset X of R^1 is *order-convex* if $a \in X$, $b \in X$, and $a < x < b$ imply $x \in X$. It is neither very difficult nor very crucial to show that the order-convex sets in R^1 are those that constitute certain familiar collections. Specifically, a set in R^1 is order-convex if and only if it is R^1 itself or is of one of the following types.

> An open ray: $\{x : a < x\}$ or $\{x : x < a\}$;
> a closed ray: $\{x : a \le x\}$ or $\{x : x \le a\}$;
> an open interval: $\{x : a < x < b\}$;
> a half-open interval: $\{x : a \le x < b\}$ or $\{x : a < x \le b\}$;
> a closed interval: $\{x : a \le x \le b\}$.

In each case, a (as well as b where it appears) stands for a constant depending on the set in question. Note that the empty set can be fitted into this enumeration under any of the last three headings by taking $b < a$, and that a singleton may be regarded as a closed interval where $b = a$.

THEOREM 39. A set in R^1 is connected if and only if it is order-convex.

This theorem can be regarded as the conjunction of two statements: (i) A set in R^1 which is not order-convex is not connected; (ii) a set in R^1 cannot be both disconnected and order-convex.

Proof of (i). If X is not order-convex, there must exist points a, x_0, and b satisfying $a \in X$, $b \in X$, $a < x_0 < b$, but not $x_0 \in X$. Then if $U = \{x : x < x_0\}$ and $V = \{x : x_0 < x\}$, $\{X \cap U, X \cap V\}$ is a disconnecting partition of X.

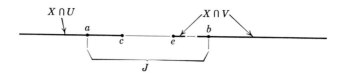

Proof of (ii). (Consult the accompanying figure, which however cannot do justice to the conceivable complexity of the situation.) Suppose that X is a disconnected, order-convex set. This will lead to a contradiction. By assumption, X has a disconnecting partition $\{X \cap U, X \cap V\}$, where U and V are open. Let $a \in X \cap U$, $b \in X \cap V$, and say $a < b$. Put $J = \{x: a \leq x \leq b\}$; J is compact (Theorem 33) and a subset of X by the assumed order-convexity of X. Therefore, $\{J \cap U, J \cap V\}$ is a disconnecting partition of J. Moreover, each of the sets $J \cap U$ and $J \cap V$, as a (relatively) closed subset of the compact set J, is compact. By Theorem 32, then, there exist points c and e in $J \cap U$ and $J \cap V$ respectively such that

$$d(c, e) = \delta_d(J \cap U, J \cap V) > 0,$$

where d is the customary metric for R^1. Therefore, if y is any point between c and e—for example, $\frac{1}{2}(c + e)$—$y \notin (J \cap U) \cup (J \cap V) = J$; hence $y \notin X$. Since $a < y < b$, this contradicts the assumed order-convexity of X.

Connected sets in R^2, to go no higher, are not so easy to characterize in some such manner as that in which Theorem 39 characterizes connected sets in R^1. In fact, connected sets in R^2 can be surprising. A moderately simple example to illustrate this comment can be constructed by putting

$$F = \left\{\left(x, \sin \frac{1}{x}\right): x > 0\right\},$$

$$Y = \{(0, y): -1 \leq y \leq 1\},$$

and taking $X = F \cup Z$, where Z is any subset of Y. *This set is connected!* In fact, F may be regarded as the graph of $f: R^+ \to R^1$, where $R^+ = \{x \in R^1: x > 0\}$ and f is defined by

$$f(x) = \sin \frac{1}{x}.$$

R^+ (with the relative topology) is connected, by Theorem 39, and therefore F is connected, by Theorem 38. It can be shown that $\bar{F} = F \cup Y$; so the italicized statement follows from Theorem 35.

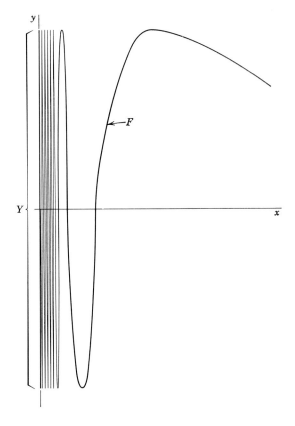

A connected set

Despite complications like this, it is possible to specify certain significant types of sets in R^n that are connected. A few instances of this appear in the next section.

According to a famous theorem of analysis, usually attributed to Bolzano, a continuous function f from an interval $\{x \in R^1: a \leq x \leq b\}$ into R^1 for which $f(a) < 0$ and $f(b) > 0$ must vanish for some x_0 satisfying $a < x_0 < b$. Bolzano's theorem is a very special case of

THEOREM 40.   If $(S, \mathfrak{I})$ is a connected topological space and $f: S \to R^1$ is continuous, then f assumes intermediate values; that is, if $f(x) = a < c < b = f(y)$, there exists a point z in S which satisfies $f(z) = c$.

Proof. By Theorem 37, $f(S)$ is connected and therefore, by Theorem 39, order-convex; and this is what the conclusion of the theorem says.

Arcwise Connectedness. A topological space which is homeomorphic to a subspace of R^1 whose ground set is a closed interval is called an *arc*. A set X in a topological space $(S, \mathfrak{I})$ is *arcwise connected* if for any two points x and y belonging to X, there exists a subspace $(A, \mathfrak{I}_A)$ of $(S, \mathfrak{I})$ which is an arc and which satisfies

$$\{x, y\} \subset A \subset X.$$

In informal terms, a set is arcwise connected if it is possible to run through any two of its points an arc that lies wholly within the set. Arcwise connectedness is a topological property.

By Theorems 37 and 39, an arc is a connected space. It therefore follows from Theorem 36 (or, more precisely, from Exercise 144) that any arcwise connected set is connected. The converse statement is false. It can be shown, for example, that the connected set $F \cup Y$ described on p. 98 is not arcwise connected. Other examples have been constructed to show that connected sets can fail spectacularly to be arcwise connected.* Simpler examples to illustrate the same point can be constructed easily by considering spaces with finite ground sets.

In spite of these examples, arcwise connectedness is sometimes rather easy to identify, for sets in Euclidean spaces especially; and then it provides a convenient basis for deducing connectedness. One general result along this line is

THEOREM 41. Any convex set in R^n (and therefore any topological space homeomorphic to such a set) is arcwise connected (and therefore connected).

A set in R^n is convex if it satisfies the following condition. If $x = (x_1, \ldots, x_n)$ and $y = (y_1, \ldots, y_n)$ belong to the set, and λ is any real number satisfying $0 \leq \lambda \leq 1$, then the point

$$(1 - \lambda)x + \lambda y = ((1 - \lambda)x_1 + \lambda y_1, \ldots, (1 - \lambda)x_n + \lambda y_n)$$

also belongs to the set. In geometrical language, a set is convex if the line segment joining any two points of the set is contained in the set. But for any two points x and y in R^n, the corresponding segment

$$\{(1 - \lambda)x + \lambda y : 0 \leq \lambda \leq 1\}$$

---

* For one of the celebrated examples of this type, see B. Knaster and C. Kuratowski, "A Connected and Connected in Kleinen Point Set which Contains no Perfect Subset," *Bulletin of the American Mathematical Society*, **33**, 106–109 (1927).

with its relative topology is an arc (Exercise 154), and since x and y belong to it while it is contained in any convex set containing $\{x, y\}$, such a set is arcwise connected.

One final example will show how Theorem 41 can be used in tandem with earlier results to establish the connectedness of a topological space. According to the description on p. 63, a Klein bottle can be defined as a certain quotient space obtained from a square in R^2; but the square is convex, and therefore connected by Theorem 41, so the Klein bottle is connected as the image under the (continuous) natural mapping involved, by Theorem 37.

Exercises

154. Show that the line segment joining any two points in R^n is an arc.

155. Prove that the unit circle is connected.

156. The unit 2-*sphere* may be defined as that subspace of R^3 whose ground set is

$$\{(x, y, z) : x^2 + y^2 + z^2 = 1\}.$$

In as many different ways as you can find, show that this set is connected.

CHAPTER SIX
uniform spaces

The primary concern of the preceding chapters has been with topological spaces. The concept of a metric space has been confronted,
but only gingerly and at arm's length; a more complete acceptance
has been avoided because the metric space concept is tainted by its
dependence on the theory of real numbers, itself a very special offshoot,
logically considered, of general topology.

The development of the theory of topological spaces, however, has
not stripped metric spaces of their usefulness. Metric spaces continue
to provide the setting for the formulation and analysis of a number of
general ideas that are not quite within the reach of general topology:
uniform continuity, for example, or the concept of a Cauchy sequence,
both of which depend on the possibility of comparing degrees of closeness throughout a space. In his thesis, Fréchet wrote: " . . . the
introduction of distance is absolutely necessary if one wants to extend
the notion of uniform continuity [from the classical setting to a more
abstract one]."* This must have been a natural thing to believe,
because it was to take more than thirty years for the contrary fact to
become widely recognized.

Efforts to develop theories within which uniform continuity and
similar ideas could be worked out, but which would not suffer from
the methodological faults of metric space theory, have moved in
several directions. One recurrent strategem has been to introduce a
"generalized metric"; that is, a function not necessarily from $S \times S$
into R^1, but into some abstract set on which a bare minimum of

* "Sur quelques points du calcul fonctionnel," *Rendiconti del Circolo Matematico
di Palermo,* **22,** 28 (1906).

suitable algebraic operations and order relations are assumed. The "metric" may then be required to satisfy the usual metric axioms (M_1)–(M_3), or some modified version of these axioms. In this way the special theory of real numbers recedes from the picture, but much of the essential mechanism of metric space theory remains. A second line of attack was embodied in the theory of uniform spaces, definitively inaugurated by A. Weil in 1937. A third was the theory of proximity spaces, introduced in 1952 by V. A. Efremovič and subsequently elaborated by others, especially Yu. M. Smirnov. The upshot is that these three approaches cover much the same ground and are far from being independent of one another. Nevertheless, the theory of uniform spaces has been much more fully developed and is more widely used than either of the others, and it is the principal subject of this chapter and the next. Nothing more will be said here about generalized metrics or proximity spaces.*

Uniformities and Uniform Structures. If (S_1, d_1) and (S_2, d_2) are metric spaces, a function $f: S_1 \to S_2$ is said to be *uniformly continuous* if, for every positive real number ϵ, there exists a positive real number δ such that $d_2(f(x), f(y)) < \epsilon$ if $d_1(x, y) < \delta$—that is, such that $f[C(x, \delta)] \subset C[f(x), \epsilon]$ for every point x of S_1. Informally, the idea is that if two points are sufficiently close together in S_1, their images will be arbitrarily close together in S_2. (The phrases "sufficiently close" and "arbitrarily close" are used here in the familiar loose way, not in accordance with the interpretive scheme of Chapter 2. The fact that, as used here, they cannot be fit into that scheme is precisely the difficulty.) It is therefore essential that there should be—as in metric spaces there is—some way of referring to the closeness of pairs of points in a comparative way. In topological spaces in general, there is no fruitful way of doing this, and there is accordingly no fruitful way of defining uniform continuity for functions from one topological space to another.

A compromise may be reached by taking the point of view that the need is for a generalization of the concept of the open ball which somehow preserves the general idea of the radius. Some index set A might

---

* The generalized metric idea appears in many forms. For one example, see G. Baley Price, "A Generalization of a Metric with Applications to Spaces Whose Elements Are Sets," *American Journal of Mathematics*, **68**, 46–56 (1941). There is still no systematic account of proximity spaces in English, but the basic ideas as well as references to some of the original literature will be found in I. S. Gál, "Proximity Relations and Precompact Structures," *Indagationes Mathematicae*, **21**, 304–326 (1959).

be picked to play the role of the set of possible radii, namely the set of positive real numbers, in metric space theory. Then for each element x of a fixed nonempty set S and for each element α of A, one might require that there should be a set $V(x, \alpha)$ which could be regarded as a generalized open ball with "center" x and "radius" α. In order to make things come out well, one would impose certain restrictions on these generalized open balls: For example, one would probably like them to form a fundamental system of neighborhoods for some topology.

A set S with such a system of "open balls" could then be regarded in a natural way as a topological space, and for such spaces one could define uniform continuity by merely paraphrasing the definition for metric spaces. In fact, if S_1 were a set assigned the system of "open balls" $V_1(x_1, \alpha_1)$ $(x_1 \in S_1, \alpha_1 \in A_1)$ and S_2 were a set with the system of "open balls" $V_2(x_2, \alpha_2)$ $(x_2 \in S_2, \alpha_2 \in A_2)$, it would be natural to say that a function $f\colon S_1 \to S_2$ is uniformly continuous (relative, of course, to the given systems of "open balls") if for every $\alpha_2 \in A_2$ there is an $\alpha_1 \in A_1$ such that

$$f[V_1(x_1, \alpha_1)] \subset V_2[f(x_1), \alpha_2]$$

for all points x_1 belonging to S_1.

This, in effect, is what is done in the theory of uniform spaces. It will be helpful to assemble a few preliminary observations before going on to the major definitions.

For each index α, a system of "open balls" of the kind just described assigns a subset $V(x, \alpha)$ of S to each element x of S, and thus defines a function from S into $\mathcal{P}(S)$; the function is a subset of $S \times \mathcal{P}(S)$. The same objectives can be reached, and more neatly, by using relations on S instead. In fact, if f is any function from S into $\mathcal{P}(S)$, then the relation

$$F = \{(x, y) \in S \times S \colon y \in f(x)\}$$

embodies f very well, because in these circumstances

$$F(x) = f(x)$$

for every element x of S. Thus, in place of the system of "open balls" $V(x, \alpha)$, one might—and usually does—prescribe a family $(V_\alpha \colon \alpha \in A)$ of relations on S, and then take $V(x, \alpha) = V_\alpha(x)$ for each possible x and α. By this time it does no harm to go another step and eliminate the index set, using merely a collection of relations on S instead of an indexed family.

A relation V on a set S will be called a *connector* if it contains the diagonal set $\Delta = \{(x, x) : x \in S\}$ in $S \times S$; in other words, if $x \in V(x)$ for every x in S. In what follows connectors are denoted by the letters V and W, sometimes with various subscripts and other distinguishing marks.

A nonempty collection $\mathcal{U}$ of connectors on a nonempty set S is called a *uniformity* on S if it satisfies:

> (U₁)   For any elements V_1 and V_2 of $\mathcal{U}$, there exists an element W of $\mathcal{U}$ that satisfies $W \subset V_1 \cap V_2$.
>
> (U₂)   For an element V of $\mathcal{U}$, there exists an element W of $\mathcal{U}$ that satisfies $WW^{-1} \subset V$.

The connectors belonging to a uniformity are sometimes called *entourages* or *surroundings*. Notice that from (U₁) and the fact that no member of $\mathcal{U}$ can be empty it follows that any uniformity $\mathcal{U}$ is a filter base (*Sets*, 43). It also follows by induction from (U₁) that if $\mathcal{U}_0$ is any nonempty finite subcollection of a uniformity $\mathcal{U}$, there exists an element V of $\mathcal{U}$ that satisfies $V \subset \cap \mathcal{U}_0$.

A uniformity that is not merely a filter base, but a filter (*Sets*, 42), is called a *uniform structure*. It is easy to show that uniform structures are distinguished from uniformities in general by having the property: If $V \in \mathcal{U}$, then any superset of V (in $S \times S$) also belongs to $\mathcal{U}$. Often it is more satisfactory to work with uniform structures than with uniformities in general, but there is value in having both concepts accessible.

Condition (U₂) is somewhat opaque to the intuition, but it can be put in a different form that may be a little more suggestive. According to the algebra of relations (*Sets*, 19–23), the expression $(x, y) \in WW^{-1}$ means that for some element y of S, there hold $(y, z) \in W$ and $(x, y) \in W^{-1}$ [that is, $(y, x) \in W$]. The two statements $(y, z) \in W$ and $(y, x) \in W$ can in turn be collapsed into $\{x, z\} \subset W(y)$. Because $(x, z) \in V$ means $z \in V(x)$, the condition (U₂) can now be restated as follows:

> (U₂′)   For any element V of $\mathcal{U}$, there exists an element W of $\mathcal{U}$ such that for all y belonging to S, $\{x, z\} \subset W(y)$ implies $z \in V(x)$.

The accompanying figure illustrates (U₂′) with R^1 in the role of S.

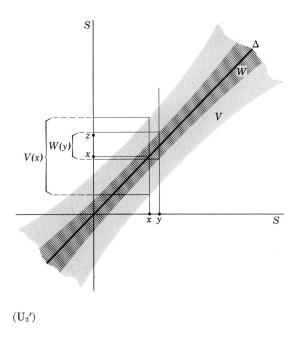

(U₂′)

It is entirely in line with the reasons for studying uniformities to take a statement of the form $v \in V(u)$ to mean that v is close to u in a specific sense represented by V. From this point of view the statement $v \in V(u)$ can be read "v is V-close to u." Condition (U₂′) can then be paraphrased in the following informal way: For any V, there exists a W such that any two points that are both W-close to some third point are V-close to each other. Similarly, (U₁) can be restated: For any V_1 and V_2, there exists a W such that if a point is W-close to another, it is also V_1-close and V_2-close to that point.

If the incentives discussed at the beginning of this section are to be consummated, metrics should give rise to uniformities in a particularly straightforward way. If (S, d) is a metric space, one would like to be able to say that the collection $\mathfrak{U}_d$ of relations

$$V_\alpha = \{(x, y): y \in C_d(x, \alpha)\} = \{(x, y): d(x, y) < \alpha\}$$

(where α is a positive real number) is a uniformity. It is not hard to verify that it is. Each V_α is a connector, because condition (M₁) on metrics guarantees that $x \in C_d(x, \alpha)$ for any x (in S) and any α. $\mathfrak{U}_d$ satisfies (U₁′), because if α_1 and α_2 are given, $V_\alpha \subset V_{\alpha_1} \cap V_{\alpha_2}$ holds if α is any positive real number smaller than both α_1 and α_2.

Finally, (U_2) is satisfied, because if α is given,

$$V_{\alpha/2} V_{\alpha/2}^{-1} \subset V_\alpha,$$

by the triangle axiom (M_3).

For a given metric space (S, d), the uniformity $\mathfrak{U}_d$ just described may be called the *standard*, or *natural* uniformity. When uniformity-based concepts are discussed in connection with metric spaces, it should be understood that the standard uniformities are the ones concerned. The connection between a metric space and its standard uniformity is epitomized by the formula

$$V_\alpha(x) = C_d(x, \alpha),$$

true for all relevant x and α.

One special property of the standard uniformities for metric spaces is that they are symmetric. In general, a uniformity $\mathfrak{U}$ is said to be *symmetric* if for every element V of $\mathfrak{U}$, $V^{-1} = V$. The symmetry of the standard uniformities $\mathfrak{U}_d$ follows directly from condition (M_2) on metrics.

The next theorem, which offers a generalization of (U_2), is frequently used in the developments that follow.

THEOREM 42. If $\mathfrak{U}$ is a uniformity, $V \in \mathfrak{U}$, and $(p_1, p_2, \ldots, p_n)$ is any finite sequence of nonzero integers, there exist connectors W_k $(k = 1, 2, \ldots, n)$ in $\mathfrak{U}$ such that

$$W_1^{p_1} W_2^{p_2} \cdots W_n^{p_n} \subset V.$$

Moreover, one can always require that $W_1 = W_2 = \cdots = W_n$.

Proof. The first step will be to prove the theorem in the special case where $n = 1$ and $p_1 = -1$. In fact, according to (U_2), there exists a W satisfying $WW^{-1} \subset V$. This W will serve as W_1; since the diagonal Δ is contained in W, $W^{-1} = \Delta W^{-1} \subset WW^{-1} \subset V$, as needed. Hence

for any V in $\mathfrak{U}$, there exists a W in $\mathfrak{U}$ such that $W^{-1} \subset V$ (and so $W \subset V^{-1}$). $\qquad\qquad$ (1)

In view of the definition of powers of relations (*Sets*, 21), it can be assumed without loss of generality that every p_k is $+1$ or -1. The proof goes by induction on n. If $n = 1$, and $p_1 = 1$, take $W = V$; if $p_1 = -1$, the existence of a suitable W is asserted by (1). If $n > 1$, and the theorem is assumed true for $n - 1$, choose first a W such that

$$WW^{-1} \subset V; \qquad\qquad (2)$$

condition (U_2) justifies this. From the case $n = 1$, there exists a connector W_n in $\mathfrak{U}$ such that $W_n^{-p_n} \subset W$, so that

$$W_n{}^{p_n} \subset W^{-1}. \tag{3}$$

At the same time, by the inductive assumption, there exist connectors $W_1, \ldots, W_{n-1}$ in $\mathfrak{U}$ such that

$$W_1{}^{p_1} W_2{}^{p_2} \cdots W_{n-1}^{p_{n-1}} \subset W. \tag{4}$$

From (2), (3), and (4) the inclusion in the theorem follows directly. Once the connectors W_1, W_2, $\ldots$, W_n have been chosen in this way, one can let W_0 be some element of $\mathfrak{U}$ such that

$$W_0 \subset W_1 \cap W_2 \cap \cdots \cap W_n,$$

and then rechoose all of W_1, W_2, $\ldots$, W_n to be W_0; the inclusion in the theorem will remain true, with all the connectors W_k equal to one another.

Exercises

157. Show that the union, the intersection, and the composite of any two connectors on S, as well as the inverse of any connector on S, are connectors on S.

158. Show that if R is a relation on S, then RR^{-1} is a connector on S if and only if $R(S) = S$.

159. Show that the aggregate of all equivalence relations associated with finite partitions of a set S (*Sets*, 37) is a uniformity on S. Sketch a few typical members of this uniformity for the case $S = R^1$.

160. For every real number r, let $V_r = \{(x, y) : x = y, \text{ or } x \geq r \text{ and } y \geq r\}$. Prove that $\{V_r : r \in R^1\}$ is a uniformity on R^1.

*161. Show that the construction for standard uniformities in metric spaces, as presented in the text, leads to a uniformity even if d fails to satisfy certain of the usual restrictions on metrics. Find an example of such a partial metric and describe the corresponding uniformity.

Equivalent Uniformities. Two uniformities $\mathfrak{U}_1$ and $\mathfrak{U}_2$ on the same set S are *equivalent* if:

   (i) For each V_2 belonging to $\mathfrak{U}_2$, there exists a V_1 belonging to $\mathfrak{U}_1$ that satisfies $V_1 \subset V_2$.

   (ii) For each V_1 belonging to $\mathfrak{U}_1$, there exists a V_2 belonging to $\mathfrak{U}_2$ that satisfies $V_2 \subset V_1$.

This defines a genuine equivalence relation on the set of all uniformities on any set S, and therefore partitions the set of uniformities into equivalence classes.

THEOREM 43.   If $\mathfrak{U}_1$ is a uniformity on S, and $\mathfrak{U}_2$ is any collection of relations on S satisfying (i) and (ii) with $\mathfrak{U}_1$, then $\mathfrak{U}_2$ is a uniformity on S equivalent to $\mathfrak{U}_1$.

The crux of this theorem is that, under the hypotheses, $\mathfrak{U}_2$ must be a uniformity; once this is known, the equivalence of the two uniformities is immediate.   The fact that the conditions (U_1) and (U_2) on uniformities, as well as conditions (i) and (ii), all are basically matters of inclusion, makes the proof straightforward.   It is therefore omitted.
   A uniformity is a filter base.   From Theorem 43 it follows easily that the filter generated by a uniformity $\mathfrak{U}$ is a uniformity—in fact, a uniform structure—equivalent to $\mathfrak{U}$.   On the other hand, two equivalent uniform structures must be equal.   Thus *there is exactly one uniform structure in every equivalence class of uniformities.*   To the extent that one chooses to regard equivalent uniformities as being essentially the same, uniform structures then adequately represent the gamut of uniformities.   From these observations it also follows that any uniformity equivalent to a uniform structure $\mathfrak{U}$ must be a base (in the filter sense) for $\mathfrak{U}$; and indeed, the term "base for a uniform structure" is frequently used for what is being called here a uniformity.

Exercises

162. Prove Theorem 43.

163. Prove that the union of two equivalent uniformities is a uniformity equivalent to both.

164. Show that if $\mathfrak{U}$ is a uniformity, then $\mathfrak{U}_s = \{ V \cap V^{-1} : V \in \mathfrak{U} \}$ is a symmetric uniformity equivalent to $\mathfrak{U}$.   Show also that if $\mathfrak{U}$ is a uniform structure, and $\mathfrak{U}'$ is any symmetric uniformity equivalent to $\mathfrak{U}$, then $\mathfrak{U}' \subset \mathfrak{U}_s$.

165. Find three uniformities on R^1 no two of which are equivalent.

Uniform Spaces.   There have already been liberal hints about the possibility of using a uniformity to define a topology on a set by way of a fundamental system of neighborhoods.   In fact, this works out very simply.   If $\mathfrak{U}$ is a uniformity on a set S, and x is any element of S, one can put $\mathfrak{N}_x = \{ V(x) : V \in \mathfrak{U} \}$.   The system $(\mathfrak{N}_x : x \in S)$ satisfies conditions (FN_1), (FN_2), and (FN_3) (p. 48) and therefore, by Theorem 11, defines a unique topology on S. Indeed, $(\mathfrak{N}_x : x \in S)$ satisfies (FN_1) because $\mathfrak{U}$ satisfies (U_1); it satisfies (FN_2) because every element of $\mathfrak{U}$ is a connector; and it satisfies (FN_3) because if $X \in \mathfrak{N}_x$—that is, $X = V(x)$ for some V belonging to $\mathfrak{U}$—then by Theorem 42 there exists a connector W in $\mathfrak{U}$ which satisfies $W^2 \subset V$, and one can take $Y = W(x)$, and for each y belonging to Y the necessary subset of X belonging to $\mathfrak{N}_y$ can be taken to be $W(y)$.

A direct description of the topology $\mathfrak{I}_{\mathfrak{U}}$ defined in this way is easily given: A subset X of S belongs to $\mathfrak{I}_{\mathfrak{U}}$ if and only if for every x belonging to X, there exists a connector V belonging to $\mathfrak{U}$ which satisfies $V(x) \subset X$. $\mathfrak{I}_{\mathfrak{U}}$ may be called, by analogy with the language for metric spaces, the *natural topology* on S determined by the uniformity $\mathfrak{U}$. It is sometimes called also the *uniform topology*. In any case, the triple $(S, \mathfrak{U}, \mathfrak{I}_{\mathfrak{U}})$ incorporates both a set with uniformity and a set with topology (in effect, a topological space). Since $\mathfrak{I}_{\mathfrak{U}}$ is completely determined by $\mathfrak{U}$, however, the symbol loses none of its definiteness by being abbreviated to $(S, \mathfrak{U})$. A pair $(S, \mathfrak{U})$, where S is a nonempty set and $\mathfrak{U}$ is a uniformity on S, is called a *uniform space*, always with the understanding that $(S, \mathfrak{U})$ is also to be regarded as a topological space, the topology in question being the natural topology that has just been discussed. At this juncture it is important to realize that it would not suffice to specify S and $\mathfrak{I}_{\mathfrak{U}}$ only; for two uniformities on the same set that lead to the same natural topology are not necessarily equal, or even equivalent.

EXAMPLE. Let S be the set of all positive real numbers. A uniformity $\mathfrak{U}_1$ may be defined on S by taking the typical connector of $\mathfrak{U}_1$ to be

$$V_{1,\alpha} = \{(x, y) : |x - y| < \alpha\},$$

where α itself is a positive real number. This uniformity is the standard uniformity given by the usual metric on R^1, of which S is a subset. A second uniformity on S, say $\mathfrak{U}_2$, can be defined by taking as the typical connector in $\mathfrak{U}_2$ the set

$$V_{2,\alpha} = \{(x, y) : |x - y| < \alpha x\},$$

where again α is any positive real number. It is a wholesome exercise (Exercise 166) to verify in detail that $\mathfrak{U}_2$ is a uniformity. The uniformities $\mathfrak{U}_1$ and $\mathfrak{U}_2$ are not equivalent: indeed,

$$V_{1,\alpha} \subset V_{2,\beta} \quad \text{and} \quad V_{2,\alpha} \subset V_{1,\beta}$$

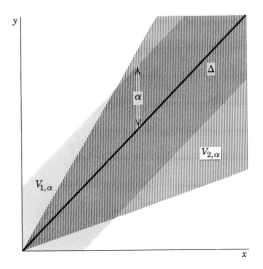

are both false, irrespective of the choice of α and β. Nevertheless, the corresponding natural topologies $\mathfrak{I}_{\mathfrak{U}_1}$ and $\mathfrak{I}_{\mathfrak{U}_2}$ are the same; in fact, they are the usual relative topology on S as a set in R^1.

Thus nonequivalent uniformities may lead to the same natural topology. Nevertheless, two uniformities that are equivalent must lead to the same natural topology. This follows directly from the definitions of uniformity equivalence and natural topologies.

There are several useful relationships between uniformities and the natural topologies that go with them, and this section concludes with the statement and proof of some of them.

THEOREM 44. If $(S, \mathfrak{U})$ is a uniform space, and $X \subset S$, then
$$\overline{X} = \cap \{V(X) \colon V \in \mathfrak{U}\}.$$

That is, a point x is an adherent point of X if and only if for every connector V of $\mathfrak{U}$ there exists a y such that $y \in X$ and $x \in V(y)$.

Proof. If
$$x \in \cap \{V(X) \colon V \in \mathfrak{U}\},$$

and $x \in U$, there exists a connector V belonging to $\mathfrak{U}$ such that $V(x) \subset U$. By Theorem 42 there exists a connector W in $\mathfrak{U}$ satisfying $W^{-1} \subset V$. From the first assumption about x it follows that there is an element y of X for which $x \in W(y)$. But then $y \in W^{-1}(x) \subset V(x) \subset U$, so every neighborhood of x intersects X in at least one point and, by Theorem 5, $x \in \overline{X}$. This establishes

$$\cap \{V(X) : V \in \mathfrak{U}\} \subset \overline{X}.$$

On the other hand, if $x \notin \cap \{V(X) : V \in \mathfrak{U}\}$, then for some member V of $\mathfrak{U}$, $x \notin V(X)$; and if $W^{-1} \subset V$ (Theorem 42 again!), $W(x) \cap X = \emptyset$; hence $x \notin \overline{X}$. This shows that the inclusion in the last display can be reversed, and is therefore actually an equality, as was to be shown.

THEOREM 45.   If $(S, \mathfrak{U})$ is a uniform space and $V \in \mathfrak{U}$, there exists a W belonging to $\mathfrak{U}$ such that $\overline{W(x)} \subset (V(x))^\circ$ for all elements x of S.

Proof.   According to Theorem 42, there exists a connector W in $\mathfrak{U}$ which satisfies $W^3 \subset V$. It will be shown that this W has the required property.   First, by Theorem 44, for any element x of S

$$\overline{W(x)} \subset W(W(x)) = W^2(x).$$

If $y \in \overline{W(x)}$, then,

$$W(y) \subset W(\overline{W}(x)) \subset W(W^2(x)) = W^3(x) \subset V(x).$$

This makes $V(x)$ a neighborhood of y, so $y \in (V(x))^\circ$ (compare Exercise 45).   Thus $\overline{W(x)} \subset (V(x))^\circ$.

Despite their origin as generalizations of the open balls in a metric space, the sets $V(x)$ in a given uniform space may well fail to be open. It is natural, then, to single out those uniformities for which all these sets are open; such a uniformity may be called an *open uniformity.*

THEOREM 46.   For every uniformity $\mathfrak{U}$ on a set S there exists an open uniformity $\mathfrak{U}_\circ$ on S which is equivalent to $\mathfrak{U}$.

Proof.   For each V belonging to $\mathfrak{U}$, take V° to be the relation on S defined by

$$V^\circ = \{(x, y) : y \in (V(x))^\circ\}.$$

Then $\mathfrak{U}_\circ = \{V^\circ : V \in \mathfrak{U}\}$ will serve the purpose.   In fact, for every V in $\mathfrak{U}$, $V^\circ \subset V$; and if $V^\circ \in \mathfrak{U}_\circ$, the W whose existence is asserted by Theorem 45 satisfies

$$W(x) \subset \overline{W(x)} \subset (V(x))^\circ = V^\circ(x)$$

for every element x of S, so $W \subset V^\circ$. According to Theorem 43, then, $\mathfrak{U}$ and $\mathfrak{U}_o$ are equivalent uniformities. Since each $V^\circ(x) \in \mathfrak{I}_\mathfrak{U}$ by construction, and $\mathfrak{I}_\mathfrak{U} = \mathfrak{I}_{\mathfrak{U}_o}$ because $\mathfrak{U}$ and $\mathfrak{U}_o$ are equivalent, each $V^\circ(x)$ belongs to $\mathfrak{I}_{\mathfrak{U}_o}$; that is, $\mathfrak{U}_o$ is an open uniformity.

Exercises

166. Show that the second uniformity in the example of this section does in fact satisfy all requirements for a uniformity.

167. Show that both of the uniformities in the example are open.

168. Determine the natural topologies corresponding to the uniformities in Exercises 159 and 160.

169. Prove that for every uniformity there exists an equivalent closed uniformity, the definition of "closed uniformity" being analogous to that of "open uniformity."

*170. Prove that for every uniformity $\mathfrak{U}$ on S there exists an equivalent uniformity which is open in the sense that each of its members belongs to the product topology on $S \times S$.

Topological Groups as Uniform Spaces. Various examples of uniformities, and therefore of uniform spaces, are indicated in the preceding sections and exercises, and other more or less isolated examples could be added. Historically, however, two major sources account for many, perhaps most, of the important uniform spaces; metric spaces (along with those generalizations hinted at in Exercise 161) and topological groups. The construction of uniform spaces from metric spaces has been discussed. An analysis of the role of topological groups in this connection requires a preliminary digression.

A *group operation* on a nonempty set S is a binary operation on S, that is, a function, say $\circ$, from $S \times S$ to S, which satisfies the three conditions (Γ_1)–(Γ_3) listed below. It is customary to write $x \circ y$ in place of $\circ(x, y)$, and this is done here.

(Γ_1) If $\{x, y, z\} \subset S$, then $x \circ (y \circ z) = (x \circ y) \circ z$. This is the *associative law*.

(Γ_2) There exists an element e of S, called the *identity*, such that $x \circ e = e \circ x = x$ for all elements x of S.

(Γ_3) If $x \in S$, there exists an element y of S satisfying $x \circ y = y \circ x = e$. This element y is denoted by x^{-1} and is called the *inverse* of x.

A pair $(S, \circ)$, where S is a nonempty set and $\circ$ is a group operation on S, is called a *group*. It is easy to show that there is only one identity in a group, and that every element of a group has only one inverse.*

A triple $(S, \circ, \mathfrak{I})$, where S is a nonempty set, $\circ$ is a group operation on S, and $\mathfrak{I}$ is a topology on S, is a *topological group* if the function $\circ$ and the function φ defined by $\varphi(x) = x^{-1}$ $(x \in S)$ are continuous with respect to $\mathfrak{I}$. More exactly, the continuity of $\circ$ is intended to mean its continuity as a function from the topological product of $(S, \mathfrak{I})$ with itself to $(S, \mathfrak{I})$. A topological group is therefore a system which can be regarded as group and a topological space at the same time, where the group operation and the topology are bound by the continuity requirements.

Examples of topological groups abound in classical and modern mathematics (see Exercises 171–173).

It is now possible to formulate a theorem that indicates how topological groups yield uniform spaces.

THEOREM 47. If $(S, \circ, \mathfrak{I})$ is a topological group, and $\mathfrak{N}_e$ is the collection of all neighborhoods of the identity e in $(S, \circ, \mathfrak{I})$, then the collection $\mathfrak{U}$ of all relations on S of the form

$$V_N = \{(x, y) : y \circ x^{-1} \in N\},$$

where $N \in \mathfrak{N}_e$, is a uniformity on S, and $\mathfrak{I}_{\mathfrak{U}} = \mathfrak{I}$.

In other words, for every topological group $(S, \circ, \mathfrak{I})$ one can define in a rather simple way a uniformity on S for which the given topology is the natural topology. Still more briefly, every topological group can be regarded in a simple way as a uniform space.

For any fixed element a of S, the function $t_a : S \to S$ defined by

$$t_a(x) = x \circ a \ (x \in S)$$

may be called, by analogy with the usual terminology for Euclidean spaces, the (right) translation by a. It is an easily verified group-theoretic fact that $y \circ x^{-1} = z$ is equivalent to $y = z \circ x$; hence

---

* For further information about groups as such, including examples, see any recent book on modern algebra or group theory: For example, G. Birkhoff and S. MacLane, *A Survey of Modern Algebra*, revised edition, The Macmillan Co., New York, 1953, Chapter 6; or Marshall Hall, Jr., *The Theory of Groups*, The Macmillan Co., New York, 1959. For references on topological groups, see Appendix 2.

$$V_N(x) = \{y : y \circ x^{-1} \in N\}$$
$$= \{y : y \circ x^{-1} = z \text{ for some } z \in N\}$$
$$= \{y : y = z \circ x \text{ for some } z \in N\}$$
$$= t_x(N).$$

Thus, under the uniformity described in the theorem, the fundamental neighborhoods of any point x are simply the neighborhoods of the identity e "translated" by x.

Proof of Theorem 47. First, $\{V_N : N \in \mathfrak{N}_e\}$ is a uniformity. It is easy to check that each V_N is a connector. If N_1 and N_2 are neighborhoods of e, then $N_1 \cap N_2$ is a neighborhood of e, and

$$V_{N_1 \cap N_2} \subset V_{N_1} \cap V_{N_2},$$

so $\mathfrak{U}$ satisfies (U$_1'$). If $N \in \mathfrak{N}_e$, it follows from the continuity of the function $\psi : S \times S \to S$ defined by $\psi(x, y) = x \circ y^{-1}$—a composite of the continuous functions $\circ$ and φ—that there exists an element M of $\mathfrak{N}_e$ satisfying $\psi(M \times M) \subset N$. Then if $\{x, z\} \subset V_M(y)$, that is, $x \circ y^{-1} \in M$ and $z \circ y^{-1} \in M$,

$$z \circ x^{-1} = (z \circ y^{-1}) \circ (y \circ x^{-1}) = (z \circ y^{-1}) \circ (x \circ y^{-1})^{-1}$$
$$\in \psi(M \times M) \subset N,$$

so $z \in V_N(x)$. Thus $\mathfrak{U}$ also satisfies (U$_2'$) and is therefore a uniformity.

It will be useful now to verify the fact, which is important in the theory of topological groups in other ways, that any translation t_a is a homeomorphism from $(S, \mathfrak{I})$ onto itself. First, the composite function $t_a t_{a^{-1}}$ is the identity map on S:

$$t_a(t_{a^{-1}}(x)) = t_a(x \circ a^{-1}) = (x \circ a^{-1}) \circ a = x \circ (a^{-1} \circ a)$$
$$= x \circ e = x.$$

Similarly, $t_{a^{-1}} t_a$ is the identity map on S. Therefore (*Sets*, 30) t_a is a one-to-one function from S onto itself, and $t_{a^{-1}}$ is its inverse. Second, t_a is continuous: If $y = t_a(x) = x \circ a$ and N is any neighborhood of y, there exist, by the continuity of $\circ$, neighborhoods M_x and M_a of x and a respectively such that

$$\circ(M_x \times M_a) = \{u \circ v : u \in M_x \text{ and } v \in M_a\} \subset N.$$
But
$$t_a(M_x) = \{u \circ a : u \in M_x\} \subset \circ(M_x \times M_a),$$

so $t_a(M_x) \subset N$, and this makes t_a continuous. Similarly, $(t_a)^{-1}$, which is $t_{a^{-1}}$, is continuous, so t_a is a homeomorphism.

Finally, $\Im_{\mathfrak{U}} = \Im$. If $U \in \Im$, and $a \in U$, then $t_{a^{-1}}(U)$ is an open set to which e belongs; therefore $t_{a^{-1}}(U) \in \mathfrak{N}_e$. But then, if $N = t_{a^{-1}}(U)$,

$$V_N(a) = t_a(N) = t_a(t_{a^{-1}}(U)) = U.$$

That is, U is a $\Im_{\mathfrak{U}}$-neighborhood of each of its points, so $U \in \Im_{\mathfrak{U}}$. This proves $\Im \subset \Im_{\mathfrak{U}}$. If $U \in \Im_{\mathfrak{U}}$, and $a \in U$, then there exists an element N of $\mathfrak{N}_e$ such that $t_a(N) = V_N(a) \subset U$. But because t_a is a homeomorphism, $t_a(N)$, and therefore U, is a $\Im$-neighborhood of a. As a $\Im$-neighborhood of each of its points, $U \in \Im$. This shows that $\Im_{\mathfrak{U}} \subset \Im$, and completes the proof.

Exercises

171. Show that if $(S, \circ)$ is any group, and $\Im$ is the discrete or trivial topology on S, then $(S, \circ, \Im)$ is a topological group.

172. Show that any Euclidean space with its standard topology provides a topological group if $\circ$ is taken to be "vector addition": If $x = (x_1, x_2, \ldots, x_n)$ and $y = (y_1, y_2, \ldots, y_n)$, then

$$x \circ y = (x_1 + y_1, x_2 + y_2, \ldots, x_n + y_n).$$

In this case, how is the standard uniformity determined by the usual Euclidean metric related to the uniformity constructed in the proof of Theorem 47?

173. Prove that the unit circle C with its relative topology and the operation $\circ$ defined by

$$(\cos \vartheta_1, \sin \vartheta_1) \circ (\cos \vartheta_2, \sin \vartheta_2)$$
$$= (\cos (\vartheta_1 + \vartheta_2), \sin (\vartheta_1 + \vartheta_2))$$

is a topological group.

174. Prove that if $(S, \circ, \Im)$ is any topological group, and $\mathfrak{B}_e$ is a base at e in $(S, \Im)$ (p. 48), then $\mathfrak{B}_e$ can be used in place of $\mathfrak{N}_e$ in Theorem 47 and its proof.

175. Show that if K_1 and K_2 are compact sets in a topological group $(S, \circ, \Im)$, then $K_1 \circ K_2$, that is $\{x_1 \circ x_2 : x_1 \in K_1 \text{ and } x_2 \in K_2\}$, is compact.

Uniform Continuity. As the discussion at the beginning of the chapter suggests, one purpose of the theory of uniform spaces is to provide a framework within which a general concept of uniform continuity can be formulated and explored. The formulation is accomplished in the manner indicated there: If $(S_1, \mathfrak{U}_1)$ and $(S_2, \mathfrak{U}_2)$ are uniform spaces, a function $f: S_1 \to S_2$ is *uniformly continuous* if, for every V_2 belonging to $\mathfrak{U}_2$, there exists a V_1 belonging to $\mathfrak{U}_1$ such that

$$f(V_1(x)) \subset V_2(f(x))$$

for all points x of S_1. It follows easily that any uniformly continuous function is continuous with respect to the natural topologies, but a continuous function from one uniform space to another can easily fail to be uniformly continuous. For example, if $(S_1, \mathfrak{U}_1)$ and $(S_2, \mathfrak{U}_2)$ are both taken to be the uniform space called $(S, \mathfrak{U}_1)$ in the example preceding Theorem 44, the function f defined by $f(x) = x^3$ is continuous but not uniformly so.

THEOREM 48.   If $(S_1, \mathfrak{U}_1)$, $(S_2, \mathfrak{U}_2)$, and $(S_3, \mathfrak{U}_3)$ are uniform spaces, and $f: S_1 \to S_2$ and $g: S_2 \to S_3$ are uniformly continuous, then $gf: S_1 \to S_3$ is uniformly continuous.

In short, the composite of two uniformly continuous functions is uniformly continuous. The problem of writing out a proof of this theorem is left as an exercise.

If $(S_1, \mathfrak{U}_1)$ and $(S_2, \mathfrak{U}_2)$ are uniform spaces, $f: S_1 \to S_2$ is one-to-one and onto, and both f and f^{-1} are uniformly continuous, f is called (among other things) a *unimorphism*. Every unimorphism is a homeomorphism, but a homeomorphism between two uniform spaces is not necessarily a unimorphism, as the example mentioned just before Theorem 48 shows. Two uniform spaces that are unimorphic (that is, between which there exists a unimorphism) should be regarded as being essentially the same from the standpoint of uniform space theory, just as two topological spaces that are homeomorphic should be regarded as being essentially the same from the standpoint of the theory of topological spaces as such.

If $(S, \mathfrak{U}_1)$ and $(S, \mathfrak{U}_2)$ are uniform spaces with the same ground set, the identity map $i_S: S \to S$ is a unimorphism if and only if the uniformities $\mathfrak{U}_1$ and $\mathfrak{U}_2$ are equivalent. From this observation and Theorem 48 it follows that if $(S_1, \mathfrak{U}_1)$ and $(S_2, \mathfrak{U}_2)$ are any two uniform spaces, replacing either $\mathfrak{U}_1$ or $\mathfrak{U}_2$ by an equivalent uniformity will have no effect on the set of uniformly continuous functions from S_1 to S_2: Any f that was uniformly continuous before the replacement will still be uniformly continuous afterward, and vice versa. The use of this remark is illustrated in the proof of the next theorem.

THEOREM 49.   A continuous function from a compact uniform space to a uniform space is uniformly continuous.

This theorem is a straightforward generalization of an important theorem of classical analysis, attributed to E. Heine, according to which a function from a closed interval in R^1 into R^1 is uniformly continuous if it is continuous.   The proof given here, which is longer than necessary, parallels one of the standard proofs of Heine's theorem, and a careful comparison of this proof with its classical counterpart will shed some light on how such proofs can be generalized for uniform spaces.

Proof of Theorem 49.   Let $(S_1, \mathfrak{U}_1)$ and $(S_2, \mathfrak{U}_2)$ be uniform spaces, the first of which is compact, and let $f\colon S_1 \to S_2$ be continuous.   In line with the remark preceding the theorem, together with Theorem 46 and Exercise 164, it will be assumed that $\mathfrak{U}_1$ is open and $\mathfrak{U}_2$ is symmetric: If they are not so at the beginning, they can be replaced by equivalent uniformities that are, and no harm is done.   Let V_2 be any element of $\mathfrak{U}_2$, and suppose that W_2 is an element of U_2 satisfying $W_2{}^2 \subset V_2$.   Because f is continuous, for each x belonging to S_1 there exists an element $V_{1,x}$ of $\mathfrak{U}_1$ such that

$$f(V_{1,x}(x)) \subset W_2(f(x)).$$

For each x, let $V_{1,x}$ be such a connector, and then choose a $W_{1,x}$ belonging to $\mathfrak{U}_1$ that satisfies $W_{1,x}^2 \subset V_{1,x}$.   The collection $\{W_{1,x}(x) : x \in S_1\}$ is an open cover of S_1, so there exists a finite subset X of S_1 such that $\{W_{1,x}(x) : x \in X\}$ is itself an open cover of S_1.   Finally, let W_1 be an element of $\mathfrak{U}_1$ satisfying

$$W_1 \subset \cap\{W_{1,x} : x \in X\}.$$

The existence of such a W_1 is assured by the remark following (U_2), p. 105.   Now if y and z belong to S_1 and $z \in W_1(y)$, since $y \in W_{1,x}(x)$ for some x belonging to X,

$$z \in W_1(W_{1,x}(x)) \subset W_{1,x}^2(x) \subset V_{1,x}(x).$$

Therefore

$$f(z) \in W_2(f(x)). \tag{5}$$

In particular,

$$f(y) \in W_2(f(x))$$

or, because W_2 is symmetric,

$$f(x) \in W_2(f(y)). \tag{6}$$

From (5) and (6) it follows that

$$f(z) \in W_2{}^2(f(y)) \subset V_2(f(y)).$$

Therefore $f(W_1(y)) \subset V_2(f(y))$ for all elements y of S_1, and this is what had to be shown.

The induction of topologies from topologies by means of functions has its exact counterpart in the theory of uniform spaces. In fact, if S_1 is some nonempty set and $(S_2, \mathfrak{U}_2)$ is a given uniform space, while f is a function from S_1 to S_2, it may be pertinent to ask whether it is possible to assign a uniformity $\mathfrak{U}_1$ to S_1 so that f is uniformly continuous. A better question, because it is more specific and proves to be just as easy to answer, is: *Does there exist a coarsest uniform structure $\mathfrak{U}_1$ such that f is uniformly continuous?*

If there were such a uniform structure $\mathfrak{U}_1$, it would need to contain all subsets of $S_1 \times S_1$ of the form

$$\{(x, y): (f(x), f(y)) \in V_2\}, \tag{7}$$

where $V_2 \in \mathfrak{U}_2$. In fact, for any V_2, there must exist a V_1 in $\mathfrak{U}_1$ such that if $(x, y) \in V_1$, then $(f(x), f(y)) \in V_2$. Then this V_1 is a subset of the set (7), and (7) itself must therefore belong to $\mathfrak{U}_1$ because $\mathfrak{U}_1$ is a filter.

To show that the answer to the italicized question is affirmative it is enough to show that the filter generated (*Sets*, 44) by the collection of sets (7) is a uniformity; because what was just shown amounts to saying that any uniform structure making f uniformly continuous must contain that filter, and clearly that filter (if a uniformity) makes f uniformly continuous. In fact, however—and this is easy to verify—the collection of sets (7) is a uniformity itself, so the filter that it generates meets all of the requirements.

The uniform structure generated (as a filter) by the collection of sets (7) is called the uniform structure *induced* on S_1 by f and $\mathfrak{U}_2$, and is denoted by $f^{-1}(\mathfrak{U}_2)$. It is a consequence of this discussion that if $(S_1, \mathfrak{U}_1)$ and $(S_2, \mathfrak{U}_2)$ are given uniform spaces, and $f: S_1 \to S_2$, then f is uniformly continuous if and only if $f^{-1}(\mathfrak{U}_2)$ is contained in the uniform structure equivalent to $\mathfrak{U}_1$.

Exercises

176. Prove Theorem 48.

177. Show that, for a given $f: S_1 \to S_2$, equivalent uniformities on S_2 induce, with f, the same uniform structure on S_1.

178. Show that the collection (7) is a uniformity on S_1.

179. Let $(S, \mathfrak{U})$ be the Euclidean line with the standard uniformity. Which of the functions from S to S defined by the following formulas are uniformly continuous with respect to $\mathfrak{U}$? *(a)* $f(x) = 0$; *(b)* $f(x) = x$; *(c)* $f(x) = x^2$; *(d)* $f(x) = \cos x$; *(e)* $f(x) = 2^x$.

180. Under the same conditions as in Exercise 179, show that f is uniformly continuous if it satisfies a Lipschitz condition—that is, if there exists a constant a such that for all x and y belonging to S, $|f(x) - f(y)| \le a|x - y|$. Find an example of a function f that is uniformly continuous but satisfies no Lipschitz condition.

181. Let $S_1 = S_2 = R^1$, let $\mathfrak{U}_1$ be the uniformity on R^1 defined in Exercise 160, and let $\mathfrak{U}_2$ be the standard uniformity on R^1. Which functions $f: S_1 \to S_2$ are uniformly continuous?

Subspaces and the Supremum. The fact, which was discussed intermittently in Chapter 4, that the process of inducing topologies by functions can be used in the construction of new topological spaces from given ones, suggests that the process of inducing uniformities might play a similar part in the theory of uniform spaces. Instead of exploring this promising suggestion, this section simply presents directly two useful concepts that might be reached by that route. Others, for example the product of a family of uniform spaces, are not taken up in this book.

The first concept is that of a subspace. If $(S, \mathfrak{U})$ is a uniform space, and X is a nonempty subset of S, the collection of relations

$$\{V \cap (X \times X): V \in \mathfrak{U}\}$$

is a uniformity $\mathfrak{U}_X$. This uniformity is called the *relative* uniformity on X, and the uniform space $(X, \mathfrak{U}_X)$ is a (uniform) *subspace* of $(S, \mathfrak{U})$. The natural topology corresponding to $\mathfrak{U}_X$ is the relative topology corresponding to $\mathfrak{I}_\mathfrak{U}$; that is, $(X, \mathfrak{U}_X)$ is also a subspace of $(S, \mathfrak{U})$ when the two spaces are considered as topological spaces, so the two uses of the word "subspace" do not clash.

Equivalent uniformities $\mathfrak{U}_1$ and $\mathfrak{U}_2$ on the same set S lead to equivalent relative uniformities on any nonempty subset X of S, but the converse is by no means true: It may well happen that $\mathfrak{U}_{1,X}$ and $\mathfrak{U}_{2,X}$ are equivalent uniformities on X even if $\mathfrak{U}_1$ and $\mathfrak{U}_2$ are not equivalent on S (see Exercise 183).

If S is any nonempty set, and $\mathbf{U}$ is a nonempty collection of uniformities on S, then $\cup\mathbf{U}$ is not necessarily a uniformity, but it is a collection of connectors on S, so there is some hope of filling it out to a uniformity. Indeed, if $\mathfrak{U}$ is the filter generated by $\cup\mathbf{U}$, then $\mathfrak{U}$ is a uniformity, and in fact a uniform structure containing all members of $\mathbf{U}$; moreover, it is the coarsest uniform structure with this property. It is called the *supremum* of $\mathbf{U}$. $\mathfrak{U}$ consists of connectors and is a filter by construction. To show that it is a uniform structure, then, it suffices to show that it satisfies (U_2). Let $V_\mathrm{o} \in \mathfrak{U}$; then by the definition of generated filter there exists a finite subcollection $\mathfrak{V}$ of $\cup\mathbf{U}$ such that $\cap\mathfrak{V} \subset V_\mathrm{o}$. For each V belonging to $\mathfrak{V}$, there exists a uniformity $\mathfrak{U}(V)$ satisfying

$$V \in \mathfrak{U}(V) \in \mathbf{U}.$$

By (U_2) as applied to $\mathfrak{U}(V)$, there exists a W_V belonging to $\mathfrak{U}(V)$ for which $W_V W_V^{-1} \subset V$. If $W_\mathrm{o} = \cap\{W_V : V \in \mathfrak{V}\}$, then $W_\mathrm{o} \in \mathfrak{U}$ and $W_\mathrm{o} W_\mathrm{o}^{-1} \subset V_\mathrm{o}$, as required.

Exercises

182. Prove the last statement in the second paragraph of this section.

183. Show that if $X = \{x \in R^1 : 1 \leq x \leq 2\}$, the relative uniformities on X obtained from the nonequivalent uniformities $\mathfrak{U}_1$ and $\mathfrak{U}_2$ in the example on p. 110 are equivalent.

184. Again let $\mathfrak{U}_1$ and $\mathfrak{U}_2$ be as in the example on p. 110. Sketch a typical member of the supremum of $\{\mathfrak{U}_1, \mathfrak{U}_2\}$ that belongs to neither of the uniform structures equivalent to $\mathfrak{U}_1$ and $\mathfrak{U}_2$.

185. If $(S, \mathfrak{I})$ is a topological space, and $\mathfrak{U}$ is a uniformity on S such that $\mathfrak{I}_\mathfrak{U} = \mathfrak{I}$, the uniformity $\mathfrak{U}$ is said to be compatible with $\mathfrak{I}$. Show that if there exists a uniformity compatible with $\mathfrak{I}$, there exists a finest such uniformity. This is called the *universal uniformity* for $(S, \mathfrak{I})$.

*186. Show that if $\mathfrak{U}$ is the universal uniformity for $(S, \mathfrak{I})$, then *any* continuous function from $(S, \mathfrak{U})$ to *any* uniform space is uniformly continuous.

Uniform Spaces and Separation Axioms.

The separation axioms listed on p. 71 lose some of their usual independence in uniform spaces. The next theorem disposes of the first three of them.

THEOREM 50.   For a uniform space $(S, \mathcal{U})$, the separation axioms (0), (I), and (II) are equivalent to one another, and to the statement $\cap \mathcal{U} = \Delta$.

Proof.   It has already been pointed out that (II) implies (I) and that (I) implies (0) for topological spaces in general.   For uniform spaces, (0) implies (II).   In fact, if $(S, \mathcal{U})$ is a uniform space satisfying the separation axiom (0) and x and y are any two distinct points of S, then either $\{x\}$ is insulated from $\{y\}$ or the reverse; say $\{x\}$ is insulated from $\{y\}$.   Then there exists a V belonging to $\mathcal{U}$ such that $y \notin V(x)$. By Theorem 42, there exists a W belonging to $\mathcal{U}$ that satisfies $W^{-1}W \subset V$.   Then $W(x) \cap W(y) = \emptyset$, for in the contrary case it would follow that

$$y \in W^{-1}W(x) \subset V(x),$$

a contradiction.   Thus $\{x\}$ and $\{y\}$ are separated by $(W(x))°$ and $(W(y))°$, and $(S, \mathcal{U})$ satisfies (II).   If $(S, \mathcal{U})$ satisfies (I), and $x \neq y$ $((x, y) \notin \Delta)$, there exists a V belonging to $\mathcal{U}$ such that $y \notin V(x)$, that is, $(x, y) \notin V$, so $(x, y) \notin \cap \mathcal{U}$.   Hence $\cap \mathcal{U} \subset \Delta$.   Since $\cap \mathcal{U} \supset \Delta$ always, $\cap \mathcal{U} = \Delta$.   If, on the other hand, $\cap \mathcal{U} = \Delta$, then if $x \neq y$, $(x, y) \notin \cap \mathcal{U}$ and so there must exist a V in $\mathcal{U}$ for which $y \notin V(x)$, and $\{x\}$ is insulated from $\{y\}$ by $(V(x))°$; thus (I) is satisfied.   This completes the proof.

According to Theorem 50, then, a uniform space must satisfy all three of the separation axioms (0), (I), and (II), or else none of them. That either case is possible is shown by the example of any uniform space whose uniformity is obtained from a metric, where all separation axioms are satisfied (Theorem 19); and by the example of a "trivial" uniform space, in which S is any set with at least two elements and $\mathcal{U}$ is the singleton $\{S \times S\}$, where the separation axioms fail.

The situation for the separation axiom (III) is simpler.

THEOREM 51.   Every uniform space satisfies the separation axiom (III).

Proof.   Let F be a closed set in the uniform space $(S, \mathcal{U})$, and let $x \in \mathsf{C}F$.   Then for some element V of $\mathcal{U}$, $V(x) \cap F = \emptyset$.   If W is the connector whose existence is stated by Theorem 45, then x and F are separated by the open sets $(W(x))°$ and $\mathsf{C}\overline{W(x)}$.

Theorem 51 can also be regarded as a consequence of Exercise 188 and Theorem 52, which follow.

A uniform space may or may not satisfy the separation axiom (IV), and there will be no theorem here on this subject.

There is yet another separation axiom, formulated and put to work some years before the introduction of uniform spaces.* Because it is not expressed in terms of the insulation or separation of sets, it does not belong directly in the hierarchy of separation axioms represented by (0)–(IV), but it must be regarded as a separation axiom nevertheless. This axiom is

TIHONOV'S AXIOM. If F is any closed set, and $x \in CF$, there exists a continuous function $f: S \to [0, 1]$ such that $f(y) = 1$ if $y \in F$, and $f(x) = 0$.

(Here, as usual, $[0, 1]$ stands for the closed interval $\{z \in R^1: 0 \leq z \leq 1\}$, and it is to be understood that the topology on it is the relative topology from R^1.) A topological space which satisfies Tihonov's axiom and either (I) or (II)—when Tihonov's axiom holds, these two separation axioms are equivalent—is said to be *completely regular*. Tihonov's axiom has been introduced only at this late stage because of its intimate connection with uniform spaces; this connection is displayed in Theorems 52 and 53.

THEOREM 52. Every uniform space satisfies Tihonov's axiom.

Proof.† According to Exercise 164 it is permissible to assume that the given uniformity is symmetric: If it is not, it may be replaced by an equivalent uniformity which is, and the resulting uniform space satisfies Tihonov's axiom if and only if the original did, because the topologies are the same.

Accordingly, let $(S, \mathfrak{U})$ be a uniform space, $\mathfrak{U}$ being symmetric; let F be a closed set in this space; and let $x \in CF$. Then by Theorem 42 there exists a sequence (V_k) of connectors in $\mathfrak{U}$ satisfying

$$V_0(x) \subset CF$$

$$V_{k+1}^2 \subset V_k \qquad (k = 0, 1, 2, \ldots).$$

* A. Tychonoff, "Über die topologische Erweiterung von Räumen," *Mathematische Annalen*, **102**, 544–561 (1929).

† It appears to be inherent in the subject that the proof of this theorem, like those of several remaining theorems (notably Theorems 53, 54, 61, and 63), must be relatively complex. Instead of being discouraged by this fact, the student should patiently work his way through these proofs, convincing himself of the validity of each step and at the same time trying to perceive the essence of the matter, thereby making the most of the opportunity to develop an appreciation of proofs more sustained than those he may be accustomed to.

(Here it is convenient to take the domain of the sequence to be $Z^+ \cup \{0\}$ instead of the usual Z^+.) Now let $t \in [0, 1]$, and express t in the binary system:

$$t = \sum_k \epsilon_k 2^{-k} \quad \text{(each } \epsilon_k \text{ is 0 or 1).} \tag{8}$$

For any t such that $E_t = \{k: \epsilon_k = 1\}$ is finite, let

$$W_t = V_{k_n} V_{k_{n-1}} \cdots V_{k_1}, \tag{9}$$

where $\{k_1, k_2, \ldots, k_n\} = E_t$, and $k_1 < k_2 < \cdots < k_n$. That is, $k_1, k_2, \ldots, k_n$ are the indices, taken in ascending order, of those terms in (8) with nonzero coefficients. Furthermore, let

$$W_0 = \Delta.$$

The rest of the proof will depend on:

CLAIM. If $t = p2^{-m}$ and $t' = (p + 1)2^{-m}$ (where p and m are non-negative integers), and $\{t, t'\} \subset [0, 1]$, then

$$V_m W_t \subset W_{t'}.$$

If p is even, all the ϵ_k's except ϵ_m are the same for both t and t'; moreover, $\epsilon_m = 0$ for t and $\epsilon_m = 1$ for t'; so $W_{t'} = V_m W_t$ by (9). Thus the claim is true in this case.

The claim for odd values of p will be proved by induction on m. If $m = 0$ and p is odd, the claim is vaculously true, because t' cannot belong to $[0, 1]$. Suppose now that the claim is true when

$$m = n - 1 \ (n \in Z^+);$$

let $m = n$ and $p = 2h - 1$ $(h \in Z^+)$. If $t'' = (h - 1)2^{-(n-1)}$, then by the inductive assumption,

$$V_{n-1} W_{t''} \subset W_{t'}; \tag{10}$$

but $V_n^2 \subset V_{n-1}$, and (by the proof of the claim for the case in which p is even) $W_t = V_n W_{t''}$; so

$$V_n W_t = V_n (V_n W_{t''}) = V_n^2 W_{t''} \subset V_{n-1} W_{t''} \subset W_{t'},$$

by (10). This proves the claim.

Now it follows easily by induction on q that if $t = p2^{-m}$ and $t' = (p + q)2^{-m}$ (where p, q, and m are non-negative integers and $\{t, t'\} \subset [0, 1]$), then $W_t \subset W_{t'}$. Thus: *If the binary expansions* (8) *of t and t' both terminate, and $t \leq t'$, then $W_t \subset W_{t'}$.* In fact, take m

to be the last index k in (8) for which $\epsilon_k = 1$ for either t or t', and put $p = t2^m$, $q = t'2^m - p$; then the conclusion of the italicized statement follows from the sentence that precedes it.

Now—to return to the main line of the proof—the function f whose existence is in question can be obtained by setting

$$f(y) = \sup \{t : y \notin W_t(x)\} \quad \text{if} \quad y \neq x,$$
$$f(x) = 0.$$

In the first of these formulas the values of t that enter are of course those for which the connectors W_t have been defined, namely those with terminating binary expansions. The set of real numbers whose supremum is taken in that formula is never empty, since 0 always belongs to it ($W_0 = \Delta$, by definition); and it is clearly bounded above.

If $y \in F$, then $y \notin V_0(x) = W_1(x)$, so $f(y) = 1$. All that remains is to show that f is continuous.

Let $t = p2^{-m}$ and $t' = (p+1)2^{-m}$, as in the claim, and let $z \in V_m(y)$. If $f(y) < t$, then $y \in W_t(x)$, so

$$z \in V_m W_t(x) \subset W_{t'}(x)$$

by the claim, and therefore $f(z) \leq t'$. Similarly, if $f(z) < t$, then $f(y) \leq t'$, because $y \in V_m(z) = V_m^{-1}(z)$. Thus the interval between $f(y)$ and $f(z)$ cannot contain an interval of the form $\{s : t \leq s \leq t'\}$. That is,

$$\left| f(y) - f(z) \right| < 2^{-(m-1)} \text{ if } z \in V_m(y).$$

This implies that f is (uniformly) continuous, and ends the proof of Theorem 52.

Theorem 53 will be virtually the converse of Theorem 52, but a bit of preliminary comment may clarify its significance. If $(S, \mathfrak{I})$ is a topological space, a uniformity $\mathfrak{U}$ on S is said to be *compatible* with $\mathfrak{I}$ if $\mathfrak{I}_{\mathfrak{U}}$, the natural topology for the uniform space $(S, \mathfrak{U})$, is precisely $\mathfrak{I}$. It has been observed in an earlier section that different, indeed non-equivalent uniformities may be compatible with the same topology. As with metric spaces (see p. 67), this suggests some questions: Do there exist topologies for which there are no compatible uniformities? If so, under what conditions do there exist compatible uniformities for a given topology?

The answer to the first of these questions is affirmative. This can be seen in one way by recalling that every uniform space must satisfy separation axiom (III) (Theorem 51), and that some topological spaces do not satisfy this axiom, as several examples in Chapter 5 show.

A topological space $(S, \mathfrak{I})$ for which there exists at least one uniformity compatible with $\mathfrak{I}$ is said to be *uniformizable;* the second question above asks for conditions for uniformizability. The preceding pages contain a number of partial answers to this question. For example, a topological space is uniformizable if it is a metric space (p. 106) or the topological space of a topological group (Theorem 47); and any uniformizable space must satisfy separation axiom (III) (Theorem 51) as well as Tihonov's axiom (Theorem 52). The condition that a topological space satisfy Tihonov's axiom is not only necessary but also sufficient for uniformizability; the sufficiency is stated by Theorem 53.

THEOREM 53. Every topological space which satisfies Tihonov's axiom is uniformizable.

The outline of the proof given next can be treated as a sequence of implicit exercises; the solutions to these exercises, taken in order, will constitute a detailed proof of the theorem. Let $(S, \mathfrak{I})$ be a topological space that satisfies Tihonov's axiom. Let $\mathfrak{F}$ be the collection of all continuous functions $f: S \to [0, 1]$.

1. The supremum $\mathfrak{U}$ of the collection of uniformities $\{f^{-1}(\mathfrak{U}_1): f \in \mathfrak{F}\}$, where $\mathfrak{U}_1$ is the standard metric uniformity on $[0, 1]$, is a uniformity on S such that all elements of $\mathfrak{F}$ are uniformly continuous, and is coarser than any other uniform structure on S with this property.

2. If $\mathfrak{U}_f = f^{-1}(\mathfrak{U}_1)$ $(f \in \mathfrak{F})$, then $\mathfrak{I}_{\mathfrak{U}_f} \subset \mathfrak{I}$; hence $\mathfrak{I}_{\mathfrak{U}} \subset \mathfrak{I}$.

3. If $U \in \mathfrak{I}$ and $F = \mathbf{C}U$, then for any element x of U there exists a V in $\mathfrak{U}$ such that $x \notin V(F)$. (Use Tihonov's axiom and the definition of $\mathfrak{U}$.)

4. Under the assumptions of 3, F is closed in $(S, \mathfrak{I}_{\mathfrak{U}})$ (use Theorem 44); therefore $\mathfrak{I} \subset \mathfrak{I}_{\mathfrak{U}}$.

From the conclusions of 2 and 4 it follows that $\mathfrak{I} = \mathfrak{I}_{\mathfrak{U}}$; that is, $(S, \mathfrak{I})$ is uniformizable with the uniformity $\mathfrak{U}$.

One particularly important class of uniformizable spaces is that of the compact Hausdorff spaces. For these spaces, the uniformizability situation is especially simple.

THEOREM 54. Any compact Hausdorff space is uniformizable. Moreover, any two uniformities compatible with the topology of such a space are equivalent.

The two parts of this theorem may be summed up by saying that there is exactly one uniform structure compatible with the topology of a compact Hausdorff space.

Proof of Theorem 54.   The second statement, which is true even with-out the assumption that the space is Hausdorff, has a quick proof: If $(S, \mathfrak{I})$ is compact, and $\mathfrak{U}_1$ and $\mathfrak{U}_2$ are both compatible with $\mathfrak{I}$, then the identity map for S, regarded as going from $(S, \mathfrak{U}_1)$ to $(S, \mathfrak{U}_2)$, is a homeomorphism and therefore, by Theorem 49, a unimorphism.   This implies that $\mathfrak{U}_1$ and $\mathfrak{U}_2$ are equivalent.

One way of proving the first statement in the theorem is to show that any compact Hausdorff space $(S, \mathfrak{I})$ satisfies Tihonov's axiom; this was done by Tihonov himself.   Another way, which has several advantages, is to construct a specific uniformity compatible with $\mathfrak{I}$. The collection $\mathfrak{U}$ of connectors of the form

$$V_\mathfrak{e} = \cup\{X \times X : X \in \mathfrak{e}\},$$

where $\mathfrak{e}$ is any finite open cover of S, is a uniformity of this kind, and the rest of the proof consists in showing that this is so.

Because each $\mathfrak{e}$ is a cover, each $V_\mathfrak{e}$ is a connector.

If $\mathfrak{e}_1$ and $\mathfrak{e}_2$ are any two finite open covers of S, the collection $\mathfrak{e}_3$ defined by

$$\mathfrak{e}_3 = \{X \cap Y : X \in \mathfrak{e}_1 \text{ and } Y \in \mathfrak{e}_2\}$$

is a finite open cover of S for which

$$V_{\mathfrak{e}_3} \subset V_{\mathfrak{e}_1} \cap V_{\mathfrak{e}_2};$$

so $\mathfrak{U}$ satisfies (U$_1$) (p. 105).

The demonstration of the fact that $\mathfrak{U}$ satisfies (U$_2'$) depends on a lemma.

LEMMA.   Let $\mathfrak{e} = \{U_k : k = 1, \ldots, n\}$ be a finite open cover of a normal space.   Then there exists a finite open cover $\mathfrak{e}_1$ of the space such that if $x_1 \in T_1 \in \mathfrak{e}_1$, $x_2 \in T_2 \in \mathfrak{e}_1$, and $T_1 \cap T_2 \neq \emptyset$, then there exists a member U_k of $\mathfrak{e}$ such that $\{x_1, x_2\} \subset U_k$.

Proof of the Lemma.   Let J be any subset of $I = \{1, \ldots, n\}$.   Put

$$X_J = \cup\{U_k : k \in J\}, \qquad Y_J = \cup\{U_k : k \in I - J\}.$$

Then $\{X_J, Y_J\}$ is an open cover, and from this it follows that $\mathsf{C}X_J$ and $\mathsf{C}Y_J$ are closed and disjoint.   Then because of the assumed nor-mality of the space, there exist open sets A_J and B_J such that

$$A_J \supset \mathsf{C}Y_J, \qquad B_J \supset \mathsf{C}X_J, \quad \text{and} \quad A_J \cap B_J = \emptyset.$$

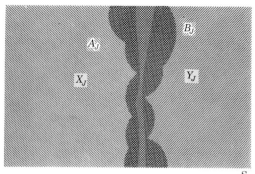

S

From these facts it follows that $A_J \subset X_J$ and $B_J \subset Y_J$; it also follows that $\{A_J, B_J, X_J \cap Y_J\}$ is an open cover. Suppose now that for each subset J of I one chooses a set Q_J which has to be one of the three sets $A_J, B_J, X_J \cap Y_J$. The intersection

$$T = \cap \{Q_J : J \subset I\}$$

is open; and the collection of all such T's, corresponding to all possible ways of choosing the Q_J's, is a finite cover $\mathfrak{C}_1$. This cover has the property required in the lemma. In fact, suppose that $x_1 \in T_1$ and $x_2 \in T_2$, where

$$T_1 = \cap \{Q_J{}^1 : J \subset I\} \quad \text{and} \quad T_2 = \cap \{Q_J{}^2 : J \subset I\},$$

and that $T_1 \cap T_2 \neq \emptyset$, but that there is no U_k containing $\{x_1, x_2\}$. This will lead to a contradiction. In fact, choose

$$J = \{k \in I : x_1 \in U_k\}.$$

Then

$$x_1 \in X_J - Y_J \quad \text{and} \quad x_2 \in Y_J - X_J.$$

Therefore $x_1 \notin X_J \cap Y_J$ and $x_1 \notin B_J \subset Y_J$. Since $x_1 \in T_1 \subset Q_J{}^1$, it must be that $Q_J{}^1 = A_J$. Similarly, $Q_J{}^2 = B_J$. But from $T_1 \subset Q_J{}^1 = A_J$, $T_2 \subset Q_J{}^2 = B_J$, and $A_J \cap B_J = \emptyset$, it follows that $T_1 \cap T_2 = \emptyset$, and this contradicts the hypothesis $T_1 \cap T_2 \neq \emptyset$. The lemma is proved.

The proof of Theorem 54 can now be resumed. $\mathfrak{U}$ *satisfies* (U₂'). If $V_{\mathfrak{C}}$ is a given member of $\mathfrak{U}$, let $\mathfrak{C}_1$ be the cover corresponding to $\mathfrak{C}$ according to the lemma. (The space is normal by Theorem 25.) If $\{x, z\} \subset V_{\mathfrak{C}_1}(y)$, the definition of $V_{\mathfrak{C}_1}$ implies that there exist sets T_1

and T_2 in $\mathcal{C}_1$ such that $\{y, x\} \subset T_1$ and $\{y, z\} \subset T_2$. Then $T_1 \cap T_2 \neq \emptyset$ because $y \in T_1 \cap T_2$, so by the lemma $\{x, z\} \subset X$, where X is some member of $\mathcal{C}$. Therefore the definition of $V_{\mathcal{C}}$ gives $z \in V_{\mathcal{C}}(x)$, as needed.

Finally, $\mathcal{U}$ *is compatible with* $\mathfrak{I}$. $(S, \mathfrak{I})$ is normal; so if $x \in U \in \mathfrak{I}$, there exist open sets O_1 and O_2 separating the disjoint closed sets $\{x\}$ and $\mathsf{C}U$. Then $\mathcal{C} = \{O_2, U\}$ is a finite open cover, and $V_{\mathcal{C}}(x) = U$, so $U \in \mathfrak{I}_{\mathcal{U}}$. This shows that $\mathfrak{I} \subset \mathfrak{I}_{\mathcal{U}}$. If, on the other hand, $U \in \mathfrak{I}_{\mathcal{U}}$, then there exists for each x belonging to U a finite open cover $\mathcal{C}_x$ such that $V_{\mathcal{C}_x}(x) \subset U$. Each of the sets $V_{\mathcal{C}_x}(x)$, as the union of those members of $\mathcal{C}_x$ to which x belongs, belongs to $\mathfrak{I}$. Thus U belongs to $\mathfrak{I}$ because it is a neighborhood (with respect to $\mathfrak{I}$) of each of its points. This shows that $\mathfrak{I}_{\mathcal{U}} \subset \mathfrak{I}$; hence $\mathfrak{I}_{\mathcal{U}} = \mathfrak{I}$, and the proof of Theorem 54 is complete.

Exercises

187. Show that satisfying Tihonov's axiom is a topological property.

188. Show directly (that is, without using Theorems 51 and 53) that every topological space that satisfies Tihonov's axiom also satisfies the separation axiom (III).

189. Find examples to show that not all compact spaces are uniformizable.

190. Prove directly that every metric space is completely regular.

191. A set A in $S \times S$ is said to be a *neighborhood of the diagonal* in the topological product of $(S, \mathfrak{I})$ with itself if there exists a set U in the product topology that satisfies $\Delta \subset U \subset A$. Show that the unique uniform structure compatible with the topology of a compact Hausdorff space $(S, \mathfrak{I})$ is exactly the collection of such neighborhoods of the diagonal.

CHAPTER SEVEN

completeness

The usefulness of the concept of a filter has been illustrated several times—indeed, much less often than it might have been—in the preceding chapters. These applications are largely by-products of the concept, which was first introduced with the definite and comparatively narrow purpose of serving as an advantageous substitute for the notion of a sequence. In this chapter the filter concept returns to this original role; and once the elements of the theory of convergence for filters have been described, it will be possible to turn to the modern theory of completeness, where the theory of uniform spaces and that of filters join in a remarkably productive way.

The Convergence of Filters. If $(S, \mathfrak{I})$ is a topological space, a filter $\mathfrak{F}$ on S is said to have a point x as a *limit* if it contains the neighborhood filter of x; that is, if every neighborhood of x belongs to $\mathfrak{F}$. The situation is sometimes also described by saying that $\mathfrak{F}$ *converges*, or is *convergent* to x.

This language is reminiscent of the theory of sequences, and with reason. If φ is a sequence in S ($\varphi \colon Z^+ \to S$), one can define a set τ_N for each positive integer N by

$$\tau_N = \varphi(\{n \in Z^+ \colon n \geq N\}).$$

Note that τ_N is a subset of S, not a subsequence of φ. It is a simple matter to verify that the collection of all sets τ_N ($N \in Z^+$) is a filter base on S. The corresponding filter,

$$\{X \subset S \colon \tau_N \subset X \text{ for some } N \in Z^+\},$$

may be denoted by $\mathfrak{F}(\varphi)$.

THEOREM 55. A sequence φ in S converges to a point x of S if and only if the filter $\mathfrak{F}(\varphi)$ converges to x.

The proof amounts to little more than a comparison of definitions, and it is left as an exercise.

According to Theorem 55, anyone who knows all about the convergence of filters in a particular space knows all about the convergence of sequences in that space. The reverse is not always true. There exist examples of non-Hausdorff spaces in which no sequence has more than one limit; that is, the converse of Theorem 28 is false. As the next theorem shows, however, if no *filter* has more than one limit, the space must be Hausdorff. Thus knowing a certain fact about filter convergence in a given space may give more information about the space than knowing the analogous fact about sequence convergence. In this sense the filter theory has a wider scope than the sequence theory. Moreover, it has a number of technical advantages, among them the fact that it does not depend on the natural number system and its properties.

THEOREM 56. A topological space $(S, \mathfrak{I})$ is Hausdorff if and only if no filter on S has more than one limit.

Proof. Suppose that $(S, \mathfrak{I})$ is Hausdorff, but that some filter $\mathfrak{F}$ on S has two distinct limits x and y. Then there exist disjoint neighborhoods U and V of x and y respectively. Because x is a limit of $\mathfrak{F}$, $U \in \mathfrak{F}$; similarly, $V \in \mathfrak{F}$. Therefore, by condition (F$_3$) for filters (*Sets*, 42), $\emptyset = U \cap V \in \mathfrak{F}$; but this contradicts (F$_1$). The filter $\mathfrak{F}$ thus can have at most one limit. On the other hand, suppose that $(S, \mathfrak{I})$ is not Hausdorff; then there exist distinct points x and y such that if $x \twoheadleftarrow U$ and $y \twoheadleftarrow V$, then $U \cap V \neq \emptyset$. From this it follows that the collection

$$\mathfrak{a} = \{X : x \twoheadleftarrow X \text{ or } y \twoheadleftarrow X\}$$

has the finite intersection property. But then $\mathfrak{a}$ generates a filter on S (*Sets*, 44), and since $\mathfrak{a}$ contains both the neighborhood filter of x and the neighborhood filter of y, the same is true of the filter generated by $\mathfrak{a}$, which accordingly has two distinct limits.

The *closure* $\overline{\mathfrak{F}}$ of a filter $\mathfrak{F}$ is the intersection of the collection of closures of the members of $\mathfrak{F}$:

$$\overline{\mathfrak{F}} = \cap\{\overline{X} : X \in \mathfrak{F}\}.$$

A point x is *adherent* to $\mathfrak{F}$ if $x \in \overline{\mathfrak{F}}$ (that is, if x is an adherent point of every set belonging to the filter).

THEOREM 57. If $\mathfrak{F}$ is a filter, $x \in \overline{\mathfrak{F}}$ if and only if there exists a filter $\mathfrak{F}'$ containing $\mathfrak{F}$ which converges to x.

Proof. If $x \in \overline{\mathfrak{F}}$, the intersection of any neighborhood of x with any set belonging to $\mathfrak{F}$ is nonempty. Therefore, as in the proof of Theorem 56, the collection

$$\mathcal{Q} = \{X : x \leftarrow X \text{ or } X \in \mathfrak{F}\}$$

generates a filter $\mathfrak{F}'$ which contains $\mathfrak{F}$ and converges to x. Conversely, if $\mathfrak{F}' \supset \mathfrak{F}$ and $\mathfrak{F}'$ converges to x, then $\mathfrak{F}' \supset \mathcal{Q}$. By the finite intersection property for $\mathcal{Q}$ (as a nonempty subcollection of a filter), the intersection of any neighborhood of x with any set of $\mathfrak{F}$ is nonempty, so $x \in \overline{\mathfrak{F}}$.

Exercises

192. Each of the following collections of subsets of R^1 is, or generates, a filter in R^1. Determine which of these filters converges and, when convergence occurs, the limit. (a) $\{R^1\}$; (b) $\{X \subset R^1 : a \in X\}$, where a is fixed; (c) the collection of all sets of the form $\{x \in R^1 : x < a\}$, where a is fixed for each set; (d) the collection of all supersets of the unit interval $[0, 1]$.

193. Prove Theorem 55.

194. Find the closure of each of the filters described in Exercise 192.

195. Show that a topological space $(S, \mathfrak{I})$ is compact if and only if every filter on S has a nonempty closure.

Completeness. In a given uniform space $(S, \mathfrak{U})$, if $V \in \mathfrak{U}$ and $X \subset S$, X is said to be *V-small*, or *small of order V*, if $y \in V(x)$ for any two points x and y belonging to X. This condition can also be expressed by saying that $X \subset V(x)$ for any point x belonging to X; or, still more simply, by saying that $X \times X \subset V$. A *Cauchy filter* on S is a filter to which there belongs at least one V-small set for each V belonging to $\mathfrak{U}$.

The notion of a Cauchy sequence in R^1 (*Sets*, 48) can be formulated in terms of the standard metric uniformity $\mathfrak{U}$ on R^1: a sequence φ is a Cauchy sequence if, for every element V of $\mathfrak{U}$, $\varphi(m) \in V(\varphi(n))$ if $m \geq N$ and $n \geq N$, N being some positive integer depending on V. This last description could be used to define Cauchy sequences in any uniform space. However, a sequence φ would be a Cauchy sequence if and only if the associated filter $\mathfrak{F}(\varphi)$ is a Cauchy filter. In line with the remarks following Theorem 55, it is therefore better to work exclusively with Cauchy filters: Cauchy filters are preferable substitutes for Cauchy sequences in just the same way that filters in general are preferable substitutes for sequences in general.

Half of the Cauchy convergence principle states that any convergent sequence in R^1 is a Cauchy sequence. The direct generalization of this statement is also true:

THEOREM 58. In any uniform space $(S, \mathfrak{U})$, a convergent filter is a Cauchy filter.

Proof. If $\mathfrak{F}$ converges to x and $V \in \mathfrak{U}$, let W be a member of $\mathfrak{U}$ satisfying $WW^{-1} \subset V$. Then if $u \in W(x)$ ($x \in W^{-1}(u)$) and $v \in W(x)$, it follows that $v \in V(u)$, so $W(x)$ is V-small. Also, because F converges to x, $W(x) \in \mathfrak{F}$. Thus $\mathfrak{F}$ is a Cauchy filter.

Unfortunately, the converse of Theorem 58 is not true generally. Those uniform spaces in which every Cauchy filter does converge are said to be *complete*. In practice, it is often easier to establish that a filter is a Cauchy filter than to establish directly that it converges; but in complete spaces doing the one is as good as doing the other. This is only one of the reasons for the importance of complete uniform spaces.

THEOREM 59. A closed subspace of a complete uniform space is complete.

Proof. If $(S, \mathfrak{U})$ is a complete uniform space, and F is a closed subset of S, then $(F, \mathfrak{U}_F)$ is complete. In fact, if $\mathfrak{F}$ is a Cauchy filter (with respect to $\mathfrak{U}_F$) on F, it generates a filter $\mathfrak{F}_1$ on S which is also a Cauchy filter, this time with respect to $\mathfrak{U}$. $\mathfrak{F}_1$ therefore has a limit x in S. This point x must belong to F, for otherwise x would have a neighborhood disjoint from F, and this neighborhood would belong to $\mathfrak{F}_1$ while being disjoint from any set in $\mathfrak{F}$, an impossible situation because $\mathfrak{F} \subset \mathfrak{F}_1$. Finally, $\mathfrak{F}$ converges to x in $(F, \mathfrak{U}_F)$. Let $U \cap F$ be any neighborhood of x in $(F, \mathfrak{U}_F)$, where U is a neighborhood of x in $(S, \mathfrak{U})$. Since $U \in \mathfrak{F}_1$ and $\mathfrak{F}_1$ is generated by $\mathfrak{F}$, there exists a member U_1 of $\mathfrak{F}$ satisfying $U_1 \subset U \cap F$; hence $U \cap F \in \mathfrak{F}$, and this is what had to be shown.

THEOREM 60. If $(S, \mathfrak{U})$ is a Hausdorff uniform space, and $(X, \mathfrak{U}_X)$ is a complete subspace of $(S, \mathfrak{U})$, then X is closed in $(S, \mathfrak{U})$.

Proof. Suppose that the hypotheses of the theorem are satisfied, but that X is not closed; then there is some point x in $\overline{X} - X$. The intersections of the neighborhoods of x with X then form a filter $\mathfrak{F}$ on X which must be a Cauchy filter (Theorem 58) and therefore, because of the completeness, must converge to some point y belonging to X. The filter $\mathfrak{F}_1$ on S generated by $\mathfrak{F}$ then converges to both x and y; but this is impossible according to Theorem 56. The supposition that X is not closed thus leads to a contradiction and must be rejected.

The exercises in the following list are really invitations to prove a few theorems, some of which are used later.

Exercises

196. Show that if $\mathfrak{U}_1$ and $\mathfrak{U}_2$ are equivalent uniformities on S, then a filter $\mathfrak{F}$ on S is a Cauchy filter with respect to $\mathfrak{U}_1$ if and only if it is a Cauchy filter with respect to $\mathfrak{U}_2$.

197. Show that, in a complete uniform space, a sequence converges if and only if it is a Cauchy sequence.

198. Show that a metric uniform space is complete if and only if every Cauchy sequence converges.

199. Let $(S_1, \mathfrak{U}_1)$ and $(S_2, \mathfrak{U}_2)$ be uniform spaces, and let $f: S_1 \to S_2$ be uniformly continuous. Show that if $\mathfrak{F}$ is a Cauchy filter in $(S_1, \mathfrak{U}_1)$, then $\{f(X): X \in \mathfrak{F}\}$ is a base for a Cauchy filter in $(S_2, \mathfrak{U}_2)$.

200. Let $(S, \mathfrak{U})$ be a uniform space, let V be a closed member of $\mathfrak{U}$, and let $X \subset S$. Show that X is V-small if and only if $\overline{X}$ is V-small.

An Extension Theorem. A problem thut occurs frequently in many settings is that of finding a continuoue extension of a given function. There are given two topological spaces $(S_1, \mathfrak{I}_1)$, $(S_2, \mathfrak{I}_2)$, a subset X of S_1, and a continuous function $f: X \to S_2$; and the problem is to find a continuous function $g: S_1 \to S_2$ which is an *extension* of f in the sense that $f(x) = g(x)$ if $x \in X$.

A problem of this character does not always have a solution. For example, if $(S_1, \mathfrak{I}_1)$ and $(S_2, \mathfrak{I}_2)$ are the subspaces of R^1 whose ground sets are respectively $[0, 1]$ and $\{x: x \geq 1\}$, $X = \{x: 0 < x \leq 1\} = [0, 1] - \{0\}$, and f is the function from X to S_2 defined by $f(x) = x^{-1}$, then f is continuous but can have no continuous extension. If there were an extension g, then $g(S_1)$ would be S_2, and since $(S_1, \mathfrak{I}_1)$ is compact while $(S_2, \mathfrak{I}_2)$ is not, Theorem 22 would be violated.

A basic theoretical problem is therefore that of finding conditions under which an extension does exist. Many interesting and useful results of this kind have been found; the next theorem embodies one of the more important ones. In this theorem it is assumed that the two spaces are uniform spaces, the second is Hausdorff and complete, $\overline{X} = S_1$, and f is uniformly continuous. In exchange for accepting all these limitations one gets not only the information that an extension exists, but also the assurance that it is unique. Because of the uniqueness especially, the theorem can be used to define functions; given f, one can define a new function g by saying that g is the function that is the continuous extension of f.

THEOREM 61. If $(S, \mathfrak{U}_1)$ is a uniform space, $(S_2, \mathfrak{U}_2)$ a complete Hausdorff uniform space, X a dense subset of S_1, and $f: X \to S_2$ a uniformly continuous function, there exists a unique continuous extension $g: S_1 \to S_2$ of f; and this extension is uniformly continuous.

Proof. First, the extension, if it exists, is unique. Suppose that g_1 and g_2 are distinct continuous extensions of f: say $g_1(x) \neq g_2(x)$, where $x \in \mathbf{C}X$. Since $(S_2, \mathfrak{U}_2)$ is Hausdorff, there exist disjoint neighborhoods N_1 and N_2 of $g_1(x)$ and $g_2(x)$ respectively. Because g_1 and g_2 are continuous, the sets $g_1^{-1}(N_1)$ and $g_2^{-1}(N_2)$, and therefore $M = g_1^{-1}(N_1) \cap g_2^{-1}(N_2)$, are neighborhoods of x. Since $x \in \overline{X}$, there exists some y in $X \cap M$. But $g_1(y) = g_2(y) = f(y)$, and $g_1(y) \in N_1$ while $g_2(y) \in N_2$; hence $N_1 \cap N_2 \neq \emptyset$, and this is a contradiction.

The remaining problem is to show that there exists an extension g. Let $x \in S_1$. The neighborhood filter $\mathfrak{N}_x$ of x is a Cauchy filter (Theorem 58), so $\tilde{\mathfrak{N}}_x = \{M \cap X: x \prec M\}$ is a Cauchy filter on X; the sets $M \cap X$ are nonempty because $\overline{X} = S_1$. Since f is uniformly continuous, the collection $\{f(Y): Y \in \tilde{\mathfrak{N}}_x\}$ is a base for a certain Cauchy filter $\mathfrak{F}_x$ on S_2 (Exercise 199). The space $(S_2, \mathfrak{U}_2)$ is complete and Hausdorff, so $\mathfrak{F}_x$ has a unique limit, which will be denoted by $g(x)$. It must be shown that the function $g: S_1 \to S_2$ so defined (i) is an extension of f, and (ii) is uniformly continuous.

(i) Suppose that $y = f(x)$, where $x \in X$. If $y \prec N$, then $f^{-1}(N)$ is a neighborhood of x in the subspace on X; that is, there exists a neighborhood M of x in $(S_1, \mathfrak{U}_1)$ such that $f^{-1}(N) = M \cap X$. Then $f(M \cap X) \subset N$, and since $f(M \cap X) \in \mathfrak{F}_x$, $N \in \mathfrak{F}_x$. Thus $\mathfrak{F}_x$ converges to y, so $g(x) = y = f(x)$, as needed.

(ii) At this point it is convenient and, in view of Exercise 196 and the remarks preceding Theorem 49, harmless to assume that $\mathfrak{U}_1$ and $\mathfrak{U}_2$ are uniform structures. Let $V_2 \in \mathfrak{U}_2$. There exist members V_2' and V_2'' of $\mathfrak{U}_2$, which can be assumed to be symmetric and closed respectively, which satisfy $(V_2')^3 \subset V_2$ and $V_2'' \subset V_2'$. Because f is uniformly continuous, there exists a member V_1 of $\mathfrak{U}_1$ such that if $\{x, y\} \subset X$ and $y \in V_1(x)$, then $f(y) \in V_2''(f(x))$. Finally, let W_1 be a symmetric element of $\mathfrak{U}_1$ satisfying $W_1{}^3 \subset V_1$. It will be shown that if u and v are elements of S_1 satisfying $v \in W_1(u)$, then $g(v) \in V_2(g(u))$, and this will establish the uniform continuity of g.

CLAIM. If $u_1 \in X \cap W_1(u)$, then $g(u) \in V_2'(f(u_1))$.

Proof of the Claim. Let N be any neighborhood of $g(u)$ in $(S_2, \mathfrak{U}_2)$; then $N \in \mathfrak{F}_u$, so there exists some neighborhood M of u such that $f(M \cap X) \subset N$. If $w \in M \cap X \cap W_1(u)$—this set is not empty because $M \cap W_1(u)$ is a neighborhood of u, and X is dense in S_1— then $f(w) \in N$, and, at the same time, $f(w) \in V_2''(f(u_1))$. Hence $N \cap V_2''(f(u_1)) \neq \emptyset$, so $g(u) \in \overline{V_2''(f(u_1))} = V_2''(f(u_1)) \subset V_2'(f(u_1))$, as claimed.

Now let $u_1 \in X \cap W_1(u)$ and $v_1 \in X \cap W_1(v)$; then $v_1 \in W_1{}^3(u_1) \subset V_1(u_1)$, so (by the choice of V_1)

$$f(v_1) \in V_2''(f(u_1)) \subset V_2'(f(u_1)).$$

But according to the claim,

$$g(u) \in V_2'(f(u_1))$$

and

$$g(v) \in V_2'(f(v_1)).$$

From these three formulas it follows that

$$g(v) \in (V_2')^3(g(u)) \subset V_2(g(u)),$$

and this was the objective.

The extension theorem has an important corollary:

THEOREM 62. If $(S_1, \mathfrak{U}_1)$ and $(S_2, \mathfrak{U}_2)$ are complete Hausdorff uniform spaces, X_1 and X_2 are dense subsets of S_1 and S_2 respectively, and the corresponding subspaces are unimorphic, then the spaces $(S_1, \mathfrak{U}_1)$ and $(S_2, \mathfrak{U}_2)$ are themselves unimorphic.

Proof. Let $f: X_1 \to X_2$ be a unimorphism with respect to the appropriate relative uniformities. Then f has a unique continuous extension $g_1: S_1 \to S_2$, and f^{-1} has a unique continuous extension $g_2: S_2 \to S_1$. Thus the continuous function $g_2 g_1: S_1 \to S_1$ is a continuous extension of the identity map on X_1. Since the identity map $i_{S_1}: S_1 \to S_1$ is also such an extension, $g_2 g_1 = i_{S_1}$ according to the uniqueness aspect of Theorem 61. Likewise, $g_1 g_2 = i_{S_2}$. It follows (*Sets*, 30) that g_1 is one-to-one and onto, with g_2 as its inverse, and therefore a unimorphism between the two spaces.

Completions. A Cauchy filter without a limit can be regarded as a filter that has the attributes of a convergent filter, except that there is no point in the space to which it converges. By definition, a complete space is one in which this phenomenon of the missing limit cannot occur. This at once suggests the possibility—and perhaps the desirability—of expanding a given noncomplete uniform space by adjoining to it extra points which serve as the missing limits. In essence this program can be carried out, and several different ways of doing it have been discovered. These processes of "completing" a uniform space can be used to define important mathematical systems. For example, in the orderly development of mathematics starting with logic, there is a point at which the rational numbers, but not the reals, have been defined. One good way of then defining the reals is to make the rational number system into a uniform space in a natural way [for each positive rational number α, define a corresponding connector V_α by $V_\alpha = \{(x, y) : |x - y| < \alpha\}$ and take the uniformity to be the set of all such connectors], and then to introduce the reals as the points of the uniform space obtained by "completing" this one.

A somewhat more careful formulation of the problem is needed, however, because the process of adjoining points is not so simple as one might hope. For one thing, the points should not be merely plucked out of the air—they should, in some sense, be constructed from the materials at hand; for another, there is the problem of defining the uniformity for the completed system, because the ground set will have changed. A workable goal is to find, for a given (presumably non-complete) uniform space $(S, \mathcal{U})$ a complete uniform space $(\widehat{S}, \widehat{\mathcal{U}})$ which has a subspace unimorphic to $(S, \mathcal{U})$. If $f : S \to \widehat{S}$ is a unimorphism from the given space onto this subspace of $(\widehat{S}, \widehat{\mathcal{U}})$, then the image $f(x)$ of any point x of S may be identified with x, and in this sense $(\widehat{S}, \widehat{\mathcal{U}})$ becomes a complete "extension" of $(S, \mathcal{U})$.

If such a complete space $(\widehat{S}, \widehat{\mathcal{U}})$ has been found, and if f is an appropriate unimorphism, then that subspace of $(S, \mathcal{U})$ whose ground set is $\overline{f(S)}$ is complete (Theorem 59), and therefore can itself play the role for which $(\widehat{S}, \widehat{\mathcal{U}})$ was intended. For this reason, no serious loss results if $(\widehat{S}, \widehat{\mathcal{U}})$ is required to have not only a subspace, but a *dense* subspace, which is unimorphic to $(S, \mathcal{U})$.

These observations lead to a definition: A *completion* of a uniform space $(S, \mathfrak{U})$ is a complete uniform space $(\hat{S}, \hat{\mathfrak{U}})$ which has a dense subspace unimorphic to $(S, \mathfrak{U})$.

Every uniform space has a completion. This fact is proved here for Hausdorff uniform spaces only. The additional restriction simplifies the proof somewhat and makes it possible to give a stronger conclusion.

THEOREM 63. Every Hausdorff uniform space has a Hausdorff completion. Any two Hausdorff completions of the same uniform space are unimorphic.

The key concept in the proof* is that of a minimal Cauchy filter. A Cauchy filter $\mathfrak{F}$ in a uniform space $(S, \mathfrak{U})$ is said to be *minimal* if it contains no Cauchy filter but itself. The proof will use the basic facts about minimal Cauchy filters listed in Lemmas 1 and 2. Here and throughout the proof it is assumed that $(S, \mathfrak{U})$ is the given Hausdorff uniform space; also, it is assumed that $\mathfrak{U}$ is symmetric.

LEMMA 1. Any Cauchy filter $\mathfrak{F}$ contains a minimal Cauchy filter; namely, that for which $\mathfrak{C}_\mathfrak{F} = \{V(X) \colon X \in \mathfrak{F} \text{ and } V \in \mathfrak{U}\}$ is a base.

Proof. $\mathfrak{C}_\mathfrak{F}$ is a nonempty collection of nonempty sets. If $V_1(X_1)$ and $V_2(X_2)$ are any members of $\mathfrak{C}_\mathfrak{F}$, then $X_1 \cap X_2 \in \mathfrak{F}$, and if W is a member of $\mathfrak{U}$ satisfying $W \subset V_1 \cap V_2$,

$$W(X_1 \cap X_2) \subset V_1(X_1) \cap V_2(X_2).$$

Thus $\mathfrak{C}_\mathfrak{F}$ is a filter base; the filter it generates will be denoted by $\mathfrak{F}_a$. $\mathfrak{F}_a$ is a Cauchy filter: If $V \in \mathfrak{U}$, $W^3 \subset V$, and X is any W-small member of $\mathfrak{F}$, then $W(X)$ is a V-small member of $\mathfrak{F}_a$. Clearly, $\mathfrak{F}_a \subset \mathfrak{F}$, so the remaining task is to show that $\mathfrak{F}_a$ is minimal. Let $\mathfrak{F}_1$ be a Cauchy filter contained in $\mathfrak{F}_a$. If $Y \in \mathfrak{F}_a$, there exist a V in $\mathfrak{U}$ and an X in $\mathfrak{F}$ such that $Y \supset V(X)$. If Z is any V-small member of $\mathfrak{F}_1$, then $X \cup Z \in \mathfrak{F}_1$; and since both X and Z belong to $\mathfrak{F}$, $X \cap Z \neq \emptyset$, and from this it follows that

$$X \cup Z \subset V(X) \subset Y,$$

so that $Y \in \mathfrak{F}_1$. This shows that $\mathfrak{F}_a$ is contained in, and therefore equal to, $\mathfrak{F}_1$; consequently $\mathfrak{F}_a$ is minimal.

---

* This proof is based on that given by A. P. Robertson and Wendy Robertson in their paper "A Note on the Completion of a Uniform Space," *Journal of the London Mathematical Society*, **33**, 181–185 (1958).

LEMMA 2.   A Cauchy filter $\mathfrak{F}$ is minimal if and only if $\mathfrak{A}_{\mathfrak{F}}$ (as in Lemma 1) is a base of $\mathfrak{F}$.

Proof. If $\mathfrak{F}$ is minimal, then (in the notation of the preceding proof) since $\mathfrak{F}_a$ is a Cauchy filter, $\mathfrak{F} = \mathfrak{F}_a$; that is, $\mathfrak{A}_{\mathfrak{F}}$ is a base of $\mathfrak{F}$.   If $\mathfrak{F}$ is not minimal, then $\mathfrak{F}_a \neq \mathfrak{F}$, because $\mathfrak{F}_a$ is minimal.

The proof of Theorem 63 itself can now be begun.   The completion $(\hat{S}, \hat{\mathfrak{u}})$ is obtained by taking $\hat{S}$ to be the set of all minimal Cauchy filters on S (it follows from Lemma 1 that this set is not empty), and then taking $\hat{\mathfrak{u}}$ to be the set of all relations on $\hat{S}$ of the form

$$\hat{V} = \{(\mathfrak{F}_1, \mathfrak{F}_2): \text{some } V\text{-small set belongs to } \mathfrak{F}_1 \cap \mathfrak{F}_2\},$$

where $V \in \mathfrak{u}$.   The required unimorphism $f: S \to \hat{S}$ will be the function defined by $f(x) = \mathfrak{N}_x$, where $\mathfrak{N}_x$ still denotes the neighborhood filter of x.   This is a suitable definition of f, because $\mathfrak{N}_x \in \hat{S}$ for every x. In fact, $\mathfrak{N}_x$ is a Cauchy filter by Theorem 58.   It is also minimal, for if $\mathfrak{F}$ is any Cauchy filter contained in $\mathfrak{N}_x$, and $M \in \mathfrak{N}_x$, then $V(x) \subset M$ for some member V of $\mathfrak{u}$.   If X is a V-small set in $\mathfrak{F}$, then $X \subset V(x)$ since $x \in X \in \mathfrak{N}_x$.   Hence $M \in \mathfrak{F}$, so $\mathfrak{N}_x \subset \mathfrak{F}$, and as a result $\mathfrak{N}_x = \mathfrak{F}$.

$\hat{\mathfrak{u}}$ *Is a Uniformity on* $\hat{S}$.   The fact that $\hat{S}$ consists of Cauchy filters immediately implies that $\hat{\mathfrak{u}}$ consists of connectors.   If V_1 and V_2 are given members of $\mathfrak{u}$, and $W \subset V_1 \cap V_2$, then $\hat{W} \subset \hat{V}_1 \cap \hat{V}_2$; if $(\mathfrak{F}_1, \mathfrak{F}_2) \in \hat{W}$, then $\mathfrak{F}_1 \cap \mathfrak{F}_2$ has a W-small element which is necessarily V_1-small and V_2-small, so $(\mathfrak{F}_1, \mathfrak{F}_2) \in \hat{V}_1 \cap \hat{V}_2$.   Thus $\hat{\mathfrak{u}}$ satisfies (U_1) (p. 105).   If $V \in \mathfrak{u}$, $WW^{-1} \subset V$, and $(\mathfrak{F}_1, \mathfrak{F}_2) \in \hat{W}\hat{W}^{-1}$, there exists an $\mathfrak{F}_3$ in $\hat{S}$ satisfying $(\mathfrak{F}_1, \mathfrak{F}_3) \in \hat{W}$ and $(\mathfrak{F}_2, \mathfrak{F}_3) \in \hat{W}$, so there exist W-small sets X_1 and X_2 belonging to $\mathfrak{F}_1 \cap \mathfrak{F}_3$ and $\mathfrak{F}_2 \cap \mathfrak{F}_3$ respectively.   Then the set $X = X_1 \cup X_2$ is V-small, and $X \in \mathfrak{F}_1 \cap \mathfrak{F}_2$; so $(\mathfrak{F}_1, \mathfrak{F}_2) \in \hat{V}$.   In short, $\hat{W}\hat{W}^{-1} \subset \hat{V}$.   This shows that $\hat{\mathfrak{u}}$ satisfies (U_2).

The Uniform Space $(\hat{S}, \hat{\mathfrak{u}})$ *Is Hausdorff.*   If $\mathfrak{F}_1$ and $\mathfrak{F}_2$ are elements of $\hat{S}$ such that, for every member V of $\mathfrak{u}$, $\mathfrak{F}_1 \cap \mathfrak{F}_2$ has a V-small element, then $\mathfrak{F}_1 \cap \mathfrak{F}_2$ is a base for a certain Cauchy filter $\mathfrak{F}$.   Then $\mathfrak{F} \subset \mathfrak{F}_1$ and $\mathfrak{F} \subset \mathfrak{F}_2$, and because $\mathfrak{F}_1$ and $\mathfrak{F}_2$ are minimal, $\mathfrak{F}_1 = \mathfrak{F} = \mathfrak{F}_2$. Thus if $\mathfrak{F}_1 \neq \mathfrak{F}_2$, there is some $\hat{V}$ belonging to $\hat{\mathfrak{u}}$ for which $\mathfrak{F}_1 \not\in \hat{V}(\mathfrak{F}_2)$. By Theorem 50, $(\hat{S}, \hat{\mathfrak{u}})$ is Hausdorff.

The Function f *Is a Unimorphism.* f is one-to-one because $(S, \mathfrak{u})$ is Hausdorff.   If $V \in \mathfrak{u}$, and $W^3 \subset V$, then for any x belonging to S, $f(W(x)) \subset \hat{V}(f(x))$.   Indeed, if $y \in W(x)$, the V-small set $W(x) \cup$

$W(y)$ belongs to $f(x) \cap f(y)$, so $f(y) \in \hat{V}(f(x))$. This makes f uniformly continuous. On the other hand, if $f(y) \in \hat{V}(f(x))$, then there is a V-small set in $f(x) \cap f(y)$, and since both x and y must belong to any such set, $y \in V(x)$. Thus f^{-1} is uniformly continuous: For any u belonging to $f(S)$ and any V belonging to $\mathfrak{u}, f^{-1}(\hat{V}(u)) \subset V(f^{-1}(u))$.

$f(S)$ *Is Dense in* $\hat{S}$. It will be convenient to prove a somewhat more sweeping statement:

$$\text{If } X \in \mathfrak{F} \in \hat{S}, \text{ then } \mathfrak{F} \in \overline{f(X)} \qquad (1)$$

The claim that $f(S)$ is dense in $\hat{S}$ follows from (1) if X is taken to be S itself; the condition $S \in \mathfrak{F}$ is automatically met for every $\mathfrak{F}$ in $\hat{S}$.

Proof of (1). Suppose that $X \in \mathfrak{F} \in \hat{S}$, and let $V \in \mathfrak{u}$. Then if $W^2 \subset V$, $\mathfrak{F}$ has some W-small element Y. $X \cap Y$ is a W-small set belonging to $\mathfrak{F}$; and if $x \in X \cap Y$, then $W(X \cap Y)$ is a V-small set belonging to both $\mathfrak{F}$ and $\mathfrak{N}_x$. Thus $f(x) = \mathfrak{N}_x \in \hat{V}(\mathfrak{F})$, so $\hat{V}(\mathfrak{F}) \cap f(X) \neq \emptyset$. Since $\hat{V}$ could be any element of $\hat{\mathfrak{u}}$, $\mathfrak{F} \in \overline{f(X)}$.

$(\hat{S}, \hat{\mathfrak{u}})$ *Is Complete.* Because of Lemma 1, it will be enough to show that any minimal Cauchy filter in $(S, \mathfrak{u})$ converges. If $\hat{\mathfrak{F}}$ is such a filter, then according to Lemma 2 the collection $\mathfrak{a} = \{\hat{V}(\mathfrak{F}): \mathfrak{F} \in \hat{\mathfrak{F}}\}$ is a base for $\hat{\mathfrak{F}}$. From this and the fact that $f(S)$ is dense in $(\hat{S}, \hat{\mathfrak{u}})$ it follows that for any $\hat{X}$ belonging to $\hat{\mathfrak{F}}, f^{-1}(\hat{X}) \neq \emptyset$; hence

$$\mathfrak{F}_0 = \{f^{-1}(\hat{X}): \hat{X} \in \hat{\mathfrak{F}}\}$$

is a filter on S. Since f^{-1} is uniformly continuous, $\mathfrak{F}_0$ is a Cauchy filter (Exercise 199). But since f itself is uniformly continuous, the collection

$$\{V(X): X \in \mathfrak{F}_0 \text{ and } V \in \mathfrak{u}\}$$

is a base for $\mathfrak{F}_0$. Therefore, by Lemma 2, $\mathfrak{F}_0$ is minimal. That is, $\mathfrak{F}_0 \in \hat{S}$. If $\hat{X} \in \hat{\mathfrak{F}}$, then $f^{-1}(\hat{X}) \in \mathfrak{F}_0$, and according to (1), $\mathfrak{F}_0 \in \overline{f(f^{-1}(\hat{X}))} \subset \overline{\hat{X}}$. Thus $\mathfrak{F}_0$ is an adherent point of $\hat{\mathfrak{F}}$, and from this it follows (Exercise 203) that $\hat{\mathfrak{F}}$ converges to $\mathfrak{F}_0$.

Any Two Hausdorff Completions of a Uniform Space Are Unimorphic. This is an immediate consequence of Theorem 62.

Exercises

201. Show that the uniform space of rationals (p. 137) is not complete.

202. Prove that in a complete Hausdorff space the minimal Cauchy filters are precisely the neighborhood filters.

203. Prove that every adherent point of a Cauchy filter in a uniform space is a limit of that filter. (Compare Theorem 57.)

Total Boundedness. In Chapter 5 the concept of total boundedness made a brief appearance in connection with the study of compact metric spaces. This concept can be defined in a natural way for uniform spaces in general: A uniform space $(S, \mathfrak{U})$ is *totally bounded* if for every V belonging to $\mathfrak{U}$ there exists a finite subset X of S such that $V(X) = S$. More generally, a set Y in $(S, \mathfrak{U})$ is totally bounded if, for every member V of $\mathfrak{U}$, there exists a finite subset Y_1 of Y such that $Y \subset V(Y_1)$.

The idea of total boundedness is important both in the deeper study and in the applications of uniform spaces. In this section, however, the idea will be developed just far enough to yield Theorem 65, which makes the relationship between compactness and completeness very clear.

THEOREM 64. A uniform space $(S, \mathfrak{U})$ is totally bounded if and only if every filter on S is contained in a Cauchy filter.

Proof. If $(S, \mathfrak{U})$ is totally bounded, and $V \in \mathfrak{U}$, let W be a member of $\mathfrak{U}$ satisfying $WW^{-1} \subset V$. Then there exists a finite subset X of S such that $\mathcal{C} = \{W(x) : x \in X\}$ is a cover of S, and each of the sets $W(x)$ is V-small. If $\mathfrak{F}$ is a filter on S, let $\mathfrak{F}'$ be an ultrafilter containing $\mathfrak{F}$ (*Sets*, 45). Since $\cup \mathcal{C} = S \in \mathfrak{F}'$, some element of $\mathcal{C}$ must belong to $\mathfrak{F}'$ (*Sets*, 46); thus $\mathfrak{F}'$ is a Cauchy filter. If $(S, \mathfrak{U})$ is *not* totally bounded, on the other hand, there exists a member V of $\mathfrak{U}$ such that $V(X) \neq S$ for every finite subset X of S. The collection

$$\mathcal{Q} = \{\mathbf{C}V(X) : X \text{ is a finite subset of } S\}$$

is a filter base on S, and the filter which it generates cannot be contained in any Cauchy filter on S. Suppose the contrary: then $\mathcal{Q} \subset \mathfrak{F}$, where $\mathfrak{F}$ is a Cauchy filter. Then some V-small set Y belongs to $\mathfrak{F}$, and

$$\mathbf{C}V(X) \cap Y \neq \emptyset \quad \text{for} \quad \text{every finite } X, \qquad (2)$$

because both $\mathbf{C}V(X)$ and Y belong to $\mathfrak{F}$. Fix a specific X, and let $y \in \mathbf{C}V(X) \cap Y$; then $Y \subset V(y)$, so

$$\mathbf{C}(V(X \cup \{y\})) \cap Y = \emptyset,$$

and this contradicts (2).

THEOREM 65.   A uniform space is compact if and only if it is totally bounded and complete.

Proof.   If $(S, \mathcal{U})$ is a compact uniform space, and $V \in \mathcal{U}$, the relation V° on S defined by $V^\circ(x) = (V(x))^\circ$ is a connector (Theorem 45). The collection $\{V^\circ(x): x \in S\}$ is an open cover of S, so there exists a finite subset X of S such that $\{V^\circ(x): x \in X\}$ is an open cover; but then $V(X) = S$.   Thus $(S, \mathcal{U})$ is totally bounded.   If $\mathfrak{F}$ is any Cauchy filter in $(S, \mathcal{U})$, then by Exercise 195 $\mathfrak{F}$ has an adherent point and therefore, by Exercise 203, is convergent.   Thus $(S, \mathcal{U})$ is complete.   Conversely, if $(S, \mathcal{U})$ is totally bounded and complete, it follows from Theorem 64 that any filter $\mathfrak{F}$ on S is contained in a Cauchy filter $\mathfrak{F}'$, and $\mathfrak{F}'$ converges because $(S, \mathcal{U})$ is complete.   Therefore, by Theorem 57, $\mathfrak{F}$ has an adherent point; so, by Exercise 195 again, $(S, \mathcal{U})$ is compact.

Notice that Theorem 65 includes the extremely important statement: *Any compact uniform space is complete.*

Exercise

*204.   Prove that any subset of a totally bounded set is totally bounded.

APPENDIX ONE

sets

In an age when the fundamental ideas of set theory are working their way well down into the pre-university curriculum, it should not be necessary to give a thorough account of them in a book of this kind. The outline that follows is intended merely to codify the concepts that are essential for the text, and to clarify some points of notation. Words and phrases in italics are being defined; the nondefinitions, with a few exceptions marked with asterisks, are statements of whose validity the reader should be able to convince himself, at least at the intuitive level.

An excellent source of more ample information on most of these matters is P. R. Halmos' *Naive Set Theory*, D. Van Nostrand, Princeton, 1960, especially sections 1–10 and 13–16.

Sets, Elements, and Subsets

1. The term "set" is properly left undefined, but it is informally understood to mean some conceptually distinct category of things. For example, one speaks of the set of prime numbers, the set of points on the circumference of a given circle, the set of differentiable real-valued functions of a real variable. Any of the "things" going to make up a given set is said to be an *element* of the set, and the relationship between a set and any one of its elements is expressed symbolically by $x \in S$ if x represents the element and S the set; this should be read "x belongs to S" or "x is an element of S." A set whose elements are themselves sets is sometimes called a *collection;* a set whose elements are collections, an *aggregate.* Elements of collections and aggregates are sometimes called their *members.* These last three

143

terms are not logically necessary, but they often contribute clarity to a discussion. $x \notin S$ means that $x \in S$ is false.

2. A set is *finite* if it is empty, or its elements can be matched in a one-to-one way with the natural numbers from 1 through some definite natural number n. A set which is not finite is *infinite*. (It is possible to define these terms without appeal to the natural numbers.) The elementary properties of finiteness and infiniteness are taken for granted here.

3. Two sets are *equal* if they have the same elements; that is, if every element of each is an element of the other.

4. A set with no elements at all is *empty*. By 3, any two empty sets are equal, so in effect there is only one empty set. The empty set is denoted by $\emptyset$.

5. The set X is a *subset* of the set Y if every element of X is an element of Y; this is expressed by writing $X \subset Y$, and also by saying that X *is contained in* Y, or that Y *contains* X, or that Y is a *superset* of X. A subset of a collection may be called a *subcollection;* of an aggregate, a *subaggregate*. The collection consisting of all subsets of a given set X is called the *power set* of X, and is denoted by $\mathcal{P}(X)$.

6. Two sets are equal if and only if each is a subset of the other. Accordingly, proofs that two sets X and Y are equal often fall into two parts: a proof that $X \subset Y$, and a proof that $Y \subset X$.

7. If X is a given set, and " . . . x . . . " represents a specific condition on x which is either satisfied or not whenever a name of a particular element of X is substituted for x, then the symbol

$$\{x \in X : \ldots x \ldots\}$$

(sometimes called the *set builder*) stands for that subset of X whose elements are precisely those elements of X for which the condition " . . . x . . . " is satisfied. For example, if X is the set of all integers, $\{x \in X : x^2 = x\}$ would be the set whose elements are 0 and 1. It is irresistably convenient to abuse this notation in various ways. For example, if it seems unnecessary in a particular context to specify X, one might write $\{x : \ldots x \ldots\}$ instead of the full $\{x \in X : \ldots x \ldots\}$. Similarly, $\{x^2 : x \geq 5\}$ (where again X is taken to be the set of integers) would be short for

$$\{y \in X : \text{for some } x \text{ belonging to } X, x \geq 5 \text{ and } y = x^2\}.$$

8. A set with just one element, say x, is a *singleton*, or the *singleton of* x, and is denoted by $\{x\}$. A set with two elements, say x and y, is called a *pair* and denoted by $\{x, y\}$; here the letters x and y are permitted to represent the same element. A finite set with the (not necessarily distinct) elements x, y, . . . , w may be denoted by $\{x, y, . . . , w\}$.

The Set Operations

9. If $\mathfrak{X}$ is a nonempty collection of sets, the *intersection* of $\mathfrak{X}$, denoted by $\cap\mathfrak{X}$, is the set whose elements belong to every member of $\mathfrak{X}$; that is, $x \in \cap\mathfrak{X}$ if and only if, for every member X of $\mathfrak{X}$, $x \in X$. The intersection of the empty collection is not defined. If $\mathfrak{X} = \{X, Y, . . . , W\}$, then $X \cap Y \cap \cdots \cap W$ may be written in place of $\cap\mathfrak{X}$; this notation is particularly useful when $\mathfrak{X}$ is a pair. If $X \cap Y = \emptyset$, the sets X and Y are *disjoint*.

10. If $\mathfrak{X}$ is any collection of sets, the *union* of $\mathfrak{X}$, denoted by $\cup\mathfrak{X}$, is the set whose elements belong to at least one member of $\mathfrak{X}$; that is, $x \in \cup X$ if and only if, for some member X of $\mathfrak{X}$, $x \in X$. In particular, the union of an empty collection is empty: $\cup\emptyset = \emptyset$. An alternative notation for the union of a finite collection is exactly analogous to that given in 9 for intersections.

11. There hold the following general associative laws: If $\mathbf{X}$ is any aggregate of collections,

$$\cup(\cup\mathbf{X}) = \cup\{\cup\mathfrak{X}\colon \mathfrak{X} \in \mathbf{X}\};$$

that is, the union of the collection made up of the sets belonging to at least one member of $\mathbf{X}$ is equal to the union of the collection of unions of members of $\mathbf{X}$. If $\mathbf{X}$ is any nonempty aggregate of nonempty collections,

$$\cap(\cup\mathbf{X}) = \cap\{\cap\mathfrak{X}\colon \mathfrak{X} \in \mathbf{X}\}.$$

12. If every member of a collection $\mathfrak{X}_1$ is a subset of some member of a collection $\mathfrak{X}_2$, then $\cup\mathfrak{X}_1 \subset \cup\mathfrak{X}_2$. In particular, if every member of a collection $\mathfrak{X}$ is a subset of the same set X, then $\cup\mathfrak{X} \subset X$.

13. If every member of a nonempty collection $\mathfrak{X}_2$ is a superset of some member of a collection $\mathfrak{X}_1$, then $\cap\mathfrak{X}_1 \subset \cap\mathfrak{X}_2$.

14. If $\mathfrak{X}$ is any collection and $X \in \mathfrak{X}$, then $\cap\mathfrak{X} \subset X$ and $X \subset \cup\mathfrak{X}$.

15. There holds the following distributive law: If $\mathbf{X}$ is a finite nonempty aggregate, then $\cap\{\cup\mathfrak{X}\colon \mathfrak{X} \in \mathbf{X}\} = \cup\{\cap\mathfrak{y}\colon$ for every $\mathfrak{X}$ belonging to $\mathbf{X}$, $\mathfrak{X} \cap \mathfrak{y}$ is a singleton$\}$. In words, instead of first forming the union of each member of $\mathbf{X}$ and then forming the intersection of the resulting collection of unions, one can equivalently first form the intersection of each collection obtainable by selecting exactly

one set from each member of **X**, and then form the union of the resulting collection of intersections.

16. The *difference* $X - Y$ of two sets X and Y is the set $\{x \in X:$ $x \notin Y\}$. If all sets in a particular discussion are subsets of one constant set S, usually called the *universal set* or the *ground set*, the difference $S - X$ is sometimes called the *complement* of X, and is denoted by $\mathsf{C}X$.

17. (DE MORGAN'S FORMULAS). If Y is a set and $\mathfrak{X}$ is a nonempty collection of sets,

$$Y - \cap\mathfrak{X} = \cup\{Y - X : X \in \mathfrak{X}\},$$

$$Y - \cup\mathfrak{X} = \cap\{Y - X : X \in \mathfrak{X}\}.$$

If Y is regarded as a ground set and $\mathfrak{X}$ consists of subsets of Y, these formulas can be written:

$$\mathsf{C}(\cap\mathfrak{X}) = \cup\{\mathsf{C}X : X \in \mathfrak{X}\},$$

$$\mathsf{C}(\cup\mathfrak{X}) = \cap\{\mathsf{C}X : X \in \mathfrak{X}\}.$$

Relations

18. A set of the form $\{x, \{x, y\}\}$ is an *ordered pair*. $\{x_1, \{x_1, y_1\}\} = \{x_2, \{x_2, y_2\}\}$ if and only if $x_1 = x_2$ and $y_1 = y_2$; so an ordered pair is completely determined by specifying its "components" x and y in order. The symbol (x, y) does this, and is usually used for the ordered pair $\{x, \{x, y\}\}$. If X and Y are sets, the *Cartesian product* of X and Y, denoted by $X \times Y$, is the set of all ordered pairs (x, y) in which $x \in X$ and $y \in Y$:

$$X \times Y = \{(x, y) : x \in X \text{ and } y \in Y\}.$$

19. Any subset of $X \times Y$ is a *relation from* X *to* (or *into*) Y. A relation from X to X is called a *relation on* X. When R is a relation from X to Y, xRy is frequently written instead of $(x, y) \in R$.

20. If R is a relation from X to Y, the relation from Y to X given by $\{(y, x) \in Y \times X : (x, y) \in R\}$ is called the *inverse* of R and denoted by R^{-1}. The inverse of the inverse of any relation is the relation itself: $(R^{-1})^{-1} = R$.

21. If R_1 is a relation from X to Y, and R_2 is a relation from Y to Z, the *composite* relation $R_2 R_1$ is that relation from X to Z defined by:

$$R_2 R_1 = \{(x, z) \in X \times Z : \text{for some element } y \text{ of } Y,$$
$$(x, y) \in R_1 \text{ and } (y, z) \in R_2\}.$$

The operation of forming composite relations is associative; therefore, if R is a relation on X, one can define powers of R by: $R^1 = R$, $R^2 = RR$, $R^3 = RRR$, and so on; and if n is a positive integer, R^{-n} stands for $(R^{-1})^n$.

22. If R is a relation from X to Y, and $A \subset X$, the *image* of A under R, denoted by $R(A)$, is the set

$$\{y \in Y : \text{for some element } x \text{ of } A, (x, y) \in R\}.$$

If $A_1 \subset A_2$, then $R(A_1) \subset R(A_2)$. If A is a singleton $\{x\}$, one usually writes $R(x)$ instead of $R(\{x\})$.

23. If R_1 is a relation from X to Y, and R_2 a relation from Y to Z, and if $A \subset X$, then $(R_2 R_1)(A) = R_2(R_1(A))$.

Functions

24. A relation R from X to Y is a *function* if, for every element x of X, $R(x)$ is a singleton. The fact that f (a more familiar letter than R in this context) is a function from X to Y is expressed by $f: X \to Y$. If $f: X \to Y$, X is called the *domain* of the function, $f(X)$ the *range*. If $x \in X$, then $f(x) = \{y\}$, where y is some element of Y; but it is conventional to write $f(x) = y$. Specific functions are commonly defined by means of an explicit expression that describes $f(x)$ for every x in the domain; for example, one might speak of "the function from the set of integers to the set of integers defined by $f(x) = x^2$." Occasionally one follows the pattern of writing $x \to x^2$ instead of $f(x) = x^2$.

25. If X is a subset of Y, the function $j: X \to Y$ defined by $j(x) = x$ is called the *injection map* from X to Y. The injection map from X to X is called the *identity map* on X and is often denoted by i_X.

26. The composite of two functions is a function. If $f: X \to Y$ and $A \subset X$, the function $fj: A \to Y$, where j is the injection map from A to X, is called the *restriction of f to A* and is denoted by $f|A$.

27. If $f: X \to Y$, $\mathfrak{X} \subset \mathcal{P}(X)$, and $\mathcal{Y} \subset \mathcal{P}(Y)$,

$$f(\cup \mathfrak{X}) = \cup \{f(U) : U \in \mathfrak{X}\},$$
$$f^{-1}(\cup \mathcal{Y}) = \cup \{f^{-1}(V) : V \in \mathcal{Y}\};$$

if $\mathfrak{X}$ and $\mathcal{Y}$ are nonempty,

$$f(\cap \mathfrak{X}) \subset \cap \{f(U) : U \in \mathfrak{X}\},$$
$$f^{-1}(\cap \mathcal{Y}) = \cap \{f^{-1}(V) : V \in \mathcal{Y}\}.$$

28. If $f: X \to Y$, $A \subset X$, and $B \subset Y$, then

$$A \subset f^{-1}f(A), \, ff^{-1}(B) \subset B, \, f^{-1}(Y - B) = X - f^{-1}(B).$$

Sets · 147

29. If $f\colon X \to Y$ and $f(X) = Y$, f is said to be a function from X *onto* Y, or simply *onto*. If, for every y belonging to Y, $f^{-1}(y)$ has at most one element, f is *one-to-one*. f^{-1} is a function from Y to X if and only if f is both onto and one-to-one. In this case, f is called a *one-to-one correspondence* between X and Y, and f^{-1} (also a one-to-one correspondence) is the *inverse function*. A one-to-one correspondence between X and X is a *permutation* of X.

30. If X and Y are two sets, $f_1\colon X \to Y$, $f_2\colon Y \to X$, $f_2 f_1 = i_X$, and $f_1 f_2 = i_Y$, then f_1 is a one-to-one correspondence between X and Y, and f_2 is its inverse.

Families

31. In many situations, it is desirable to regard the elements of the range of a function as elements of an "indexed set," the domain providing the indices: If $f\colon X \to Y$, one may write y_x instead of $f(x)$. With this emphasis, f is called a *family* in Y, and X is called the *index set* of the family. A family may be denoted by an adaptation of the set builder: $(y_x\colon x \in X)$. It is important to distinguish $(y_x\colon x \in X)$, the family itself and therefore a function, from $\{y_x\colon x \in X\}$, the range of this function. Any set X may be treated as a family by taking X itself as the index set and taking the identity map as the function. Such a family, naturally denoted by $(x\colon x \in X)$, is sometimes called a *self-indexed* family. When the index set of a family consists of the first n positive integers, the family may be denoted by $(y_1, \ldots, y_n)$, or by the same expression with some appropriate symbol in place of y.

32. A family $f\colon X \to Y$ for which the index set X is Z^+, the set of positive integers, is called a *sequence* in Y. If $g\colon Z^+ \to Z^+$ is a strictly increasing function [that is, if $m \in Z^+$, $n \in Z^+$, and $m < n$, then $g(m) < g(n)$], then the composite function $fg\colon Z^+ \to Y$ [or $(y_{n_k}\colon k \in Z^+)$, where $n_k = g(k)$] is a *subsequence* of f.

33. If $\mathfrak{X}$ is a collection, and $(X_\alpha\colon \alpha \in A)$ is a family in $\mathfrak{X}$ with the index set A, the set of all functions $\varphi\colon A \to \cup \mathfrak{X}$ which satisfy, for every index α, $\varphi(\alpha) \in X_\alpha$, is called the *Cartesian product* of the family and is denoted by $\times_\alpha (X_\alpha\colon \alpha \in A)$ or simply $\times_\alpha X_\alpha$. If A is finite, $A = \{\alpha, \beta, \ldots, \lambda\}$, an alternative notation is $X_\alpha \times X_\beta \times \cdots \times X_\lambda$. When A has just two elements, this notion of Cartesian product and that of 18, although not identical, are essentially the same and can be used interchangeably. Note that any element of $\times_\alpha (X_\alpha\colon \alpha \in A)$ is itself a family with the index set A.

Equivalence Relations

34. A relation E on a set X is an *equivalence relation* if it satisfies:

(E_1) (Reflexivity) For every x belonging to X, $(x, x) \in E$ (that is, $i_X \subset E$).

(E_2) (Symmetry) For every x and y belonging to X, if $(x, y) \in E$, then $(y, x) \in E$ (that is, $E \subset E^{-1}$).

(E_3) (Transitivity) For every x, y, and z belonging to X, if $(x, y) \in E$ and $(y, z) \in E$, then $(x, z) \in E$ (that is, $E^2 \subset E$).

35. If E is an equivalence relation on X, and $x \in X$, the set $E(x)$ is called the *equivalence class* of x. For every x, $x \in E(x)$, so equivalence classes are not empty. The collection of all equivalence classes $\{E(x) : x \in X\}$ is called the *quotient set of X by E* and is denoted by X/E.

36. A collection $\mathfrak{X}$ whose members are subsets of a set X is a *partition* of X if $\cup \mathfrak{X} = X$ and, for any two members A and B of $\mathfrak{X}$, $A \cap B \neq \emptyset$ implies $A = B$. It is frequently, but not always, convenient to stipulate that the members of a partition should be nonempty.

37. The quotient set of a set X by an equivalence relation E on X is a partition of X. If $\mathfrak{X}$ is a partition of X, and $\emptyset \notin \mathfrak{X}$, the relation

$$\{(x, y) : \text{for some member } A \text{ of } \mathfrak{X}, \{x, y\} \subset A\}$$

or equivalently

$$\cup\{A \times A : A \in \mathfrak{X}\}$$

is an equivalence relation on X for which the corresponding equivalence classes are precisely the members of X. An equivalence relation and the partition corresponding to each other in this way are said to be *associated*.

The Axiom of Choice. Zermelo's axiom of choice, for which a remarkable number of alternative formulations have now been found, seems innocuous enough until one hears of some of its consequences. Nevertheless, topologists tend to use it more or less unquestioningly, and often tacitly. Which formulation is most convenient depends on the context; the three listed in paragraphs 38, 39, and 41 are adequate for the needs of this book. The third, Zorn's lemma, is given in a specialized form.

*38. If $\mathfrak{X}$ is a nonempty collection, $\emptyset \notin \mathfrak{X}$, and any two distinct members of $\mathfrak{X}$ are disjoint, then there exists a set A with the property that, for every member X of $\mathfrak{X}$, $A \cap X$ is a singleton.

*39. If $(X_\alpha\colon \alpha \in A)$ is a family of sets where, for every index α, $X_\alpha \neq \emptyset$, then the Cartesian product $\times_\alpha X_\alpha$ is not empty.

40. A collection $\mathfrak{X}$ of sets is *totally ordered* if, for any two members X and Y of $\mathfrak{X}$, either $X \subset Y$ or $Y \subset X$. A member A of $\mathfrak{X}$ is *maximal* if the only superset of A belonging to $\mathfrak{X}$ is A itself. If $\mathfrak{a}$ is a sub-collection of $\mathfrak{X}$, any member of $\mathfrak{X}$ which contains $\cup \mathfrak{a}$ is an *upper bound* of $\mathfrak{a}$ in $\mathfrak{X}$. Strictly speaking, each of the three phrases defined here should be followed by some such phrase as "with respect to $\subset$"; the unqualified terms have a more general meaning. Nevertheless, in this book the terms are used in connection with collections in no other way, so the abbreviation is legitimate.

*41. (ZORN'S LEMMA). If every totally ordered subcollection of a nonempty collection $\mathfrak{X}$ has an upper bound in $\mathfrak{X}$, then $\mathfrak{X}$ has a maximal element.

Filters. The theory of filters is not usually regarded as a part of set theory, and books on set theory do not ordinarily mention it. For this reason, paragraphs 42 through 46 are somewhat more detailed than earlier paragraphs. For further information on filters, see the work by Bourbaki cited in Appendix 2.

42. If S is a nonempty set, a *filter* on S is a nonempty collection $\mathfrak{F}$ of subsets of S with the properties:

(F_1) $\emptyset \notin \mathfrak{F}$.
(F_2) For any two subsets X and Y of S, if $X \in \mathfrak{F}$ and $X \subset Y$, then $Y \in \mathfrak{F}$.
(F_3) For any two members X and Y of $\mathfrak{F}$, $X \cap Y \in \mathfrak{F}$.

It follows from (F_3) by mathematical induction that the intersection of any nonempty finite subcollection of a filter $\mathfrak{F}$ belongs to $\mathfrak{F}$. From this in turn, and (F_1), it follows that any filter (indeed, any subcollection of a filter) has the *finite intersection property:* The intersection of any nonempty finite subcollection is nonempty. The intersection of any nonempty aggregate of filters on S is a filter on S.

EXAMPLES OF FILTERS. If S is a nonempty set and X is a nonempty subset of S, then the collection $\{Y \subset S\colon X \subset Y\}$ is a filter on S. The collection of all relations on a nonempty set X which satisfy (E_1) (see 34) is a filter on $X \times X$. If S is an infinite set, the collection $\{X \subset S\colon$

$S - X$ is finite} is a filter on S. (Note that the intersection of this filter is $\emptyset$.)

43. A subcollection $\mathfrak{B}$ of a filter $\mathfrak{F}$ on S is a *base* of $\mathfrak{F}$ if

$$\mathfrak{F} = \{X \subset S : \text{for some member } Y \text{ of } \mathfrak{B}, \, Y \subset X\}.$$

A nonempty collection $\mathfrak{B}$ of subsets of S is a base of some filter on S (namely, the collection $\mathfrak{F}$ given by the formula), if and only if

(FB$_1$) $\emptyset \notin \mathfrak{B}$;
(FB$_2$)   the intersection of any two members of $\mathfrak{B}$ contains a member of $\mathfrak{B}$.

44. If a nonempty collection $\mathfrak{a}$ of subsets of a nonempty set S is contained in any filter on S at all, then the intersection of the aggregate of all filters on S which contain $\mathfrak{a}$ is such a filter, and is said to be the filter *generated* by $\mathfrak{a}$. A collection $\mathfrak{a}$ generates a filter if and only if it has the finite intersection property. The condition is necessary, because any subcollection of a filter must have this property; it is sufficient, because $\mathfrak{B} = \{\cap \mathfrak{x} : \mathfrak{x} \text{ is a finite nonempty subcollection of } \mathfrak{a}\}$ is then a filter base, and the filter of which it is a base contains $\mathfrak{a}$—indeed, is the filter generated by $\mathfrak{a}$. In particular, any filter base generates the filter of which it is a base.

45. A filter on S which is maximal in the aggregate of all filters on S is an *ultrafilter*. Every filter $\mathfrak{F}$ is contained in an ultrafilter: If **F** is the aggregate of filters on S containing $\mathfrak{F}$, every totally ordered subaggregate **G** of **F** has an upper bound, namely $\cup$**G**. Hence (by 41) **F** has a maximal member $\mathfrak{F}_1$, and this must also be a maximal member of the aggregate of all filters on S—that is, an ultrafilter.

46. If $\mathfrak{F}$ is an ultrafilter on S, and $\mathfrak{x}$ is a finite collection of subsets of S such that $\cup \mathfrak{x} \in \mathfrak{F}$, then $\mathfrak{F} \cap \mathfrak{x} \neq \emptyset$.
Proof. Let X be a nonempty member of $\mathfrak{x}$, and let $\tilde{X} = \cup(\mathfrak{x} - \{X\})$. If $\tilde{X} = \emptyset$, then $X = \cup \mathfrak{x} \in \mathfrak{F}$, and there is nothing more to prove. So let $\tilde{X} \neq \emptyset$, and assume that neither X nor $\tilde{X}$ belongs to $\mathfrak{F}$. Let $\mathfrak{F}_1 = \{Y \subset S : X \cup Y \in \mathfrak{F}\}$. $\mathfrak{F}_1$ is a filter containing $\mathfrak{F}$, but $\mathfrak{F}_1 \neq \mathfrak{F}$, since $\tilde{X} \in \mathfrak{F}_1 - \mathfrak{F}$. Hence $\mathfrak{F}$ is not maximal, and this contradiction implies that either $X \in \mathfrak{F}$ or $\tilde{X} \in \mathfrak{F}$. In the former case, the proof is ended; in the latter, the argument can be repeated with $\mathfrak{x} - \{X\}$ in place of $\mathfrak{x}$. Since $\mathfrak{x}$ is finite, a sufficient number of repetitions of the argument will lead to the conclusion that some member of $\mathfrak{x}$ belongs to $\mathfrak{F}$.

Real Numbers. The real number system appears frequently in this book, but almost always incidentally—in examples, exercises, and digressions. (Its most serious appearance is in the discussion of Tihonov's axiom in Chapter 6.) Moreover, the reader is surely well acquainted with all the elementary facts about this system. There should therefore be no need to include here, even in outline, a rigorous survey of the subject. Nevertheless, the very few facts about the real number system listed here may be useful for reference, although they are certainly no part of set theory.

∗47. Let R be the set of real numbers. An element b of R is an *upper bound* of a subset X of R if $x \le b$ for all elements x of X. If X is a nonempty set with at least one upper bound, the set $\{b \in R : b$ is an upper bound of $X\}$ has a smallest element, called the *supremum* of X and denoted by sup X. *Lower bound* and *infimum* are defined analogously, with the inequalities reversed. The infimum of X is denoted by inf X. If $b = \sup X$, then for any positive real number ϵ,

$$X \cap \{y \in R : b - \epsilon < y \le b\} \ne \emptyset.$$

Similarly, if $a = \inf X$,

$$X \cap \{y \in R : a \le y < a + \epsilon\} \ne \emptyset.$$

48. A sequence $(x_n : n \in Z^+)$ in R is a *Cauchy sequence* if, for every positive real number ϵ, there exists an element N of Z^+ such that if $m \ge N$ and $n \ge N$, then $|x_m - x_n| < \epsilon$.

49. (CAUCHY CONVERGENCE PRINCIPLE). A sequence in R converges if and only if it is a Cauchy sequence.

APPENDIX TWO
suggested further reading

The material presented in this book is more nearly a beginning than an end; it can be used as a point of departure for the study of a variety of more advanced books on the same subject, or on other subjects that have a basis in general topology. This appendix contains a few suggestions about reading that might be done along these lines, but the books mentioned come nowhere near exhausting the possibilities. Many of these books contain preliminary material on general topology (indeed, the presence of such material is usually a reliable indication of the extent to which general topology is used in the book); much of this material you will now be able to skim or skip. One general note of caution should be sounded. The usage of terminology and notation is by no means uniform and usually must be checked. One term (for example, "topological space") may be found with many different meanings, and one concept (for instance, that of a cluster point) may be found with many different names.

General Topology. There are several recent treatises on general topology which are considerably more comprehensive than this book; some of them use a markedly different approach to the subject. Among them are:

N. Bourbaki, *Éléments de mathématique, premiére partie, Livre* III: *Topologie Générale*, Hermann & Cie., Paris, various editions and dates: especially Chapters I, II, and IX. (An English translation is in preparation.) To the extent that the development of general topology in the present book has a model—and the extent is large—the model is Bourbaki's. Other parts of the *Éléments* deal with many of the topics mentioned later, but further particular references to Bourbaki are not given.

J. L. Kelley, *General Topology*, D. Van Nostrand, Princeton, 1955. An interesting feature of this book is the use of the theory of nets instead of the theory of filters.

H.-J. Kowalsky, *Topologische Räume*, Birkhäuser Verlag, Basel and Stuttgart, 1961.

C. Kuratowski, *Topologie*, Monografie Matematyczne, Warsaw, various editions and dates; 2 volumes. This work, in French, differs considerably in notation and otherwise from most recent writings on the subject, but it is a treasure-house of information.

W. Sierpinski, *General Topology*, University of Toronto Press, Toronto, 1952. The greater part of this book is concerned with the topology of metric spaces.

Two books that may appeal especially to those who are interested in the axiomatics of general topology and in possible generalizations of the concept of a topological space are:

A. Appert, *Propriétés des espaces abstraits les plus généraux*, Hermann & Cie., Paris, 1934; 2 volumes.

Á. Császár, *Fondements de la topologie générale*, Gauthier-Villars, Paris, 1960.

A book that is important for its novel treatment of uniform spaces is

J. W. Tukey, *Convergence and Uniformity in Topology*, Princeton University Press, Princeton, 1940.

Algebraic Topology. In algebraic topology one undertakes to characterize certain topological spaces with the aid of associated algebraic systems, usually groups. The algebraic side of this subject tends to predominate more and more, but the ideas of general topology continue to play their role.

P. S. Aleksandrov, *Combinatorial Topology*, Graylock Press, Rochester and Albany, 1956–1960, 3 volumes.

S. Lefschetz, *Introduction to Topology*, Princeton University Press, Princeton, 1949.

A. H. Wallace, *Algebraic Topology*, Pergamon Press, New York, 1957.

Topological Algebra. The topological group, briefly introduced in Chapter 6, is a specimen of the mixture of topological and algebraic ideas that has led to a number of interesting theories; and the oldest and most important of these theories is perhaps that of the topological groups themselves. Two standard works are

L. Pontrjagin, *Topological Groups*, Princeton University Press, Princeton, 1939. A second Russian edition, for which there is a German translation, was published in 1954.

A. Weil, *L'Intégration dans les groupes topologiques et ses applications*, Hermann & Cie., Paris, second edition, 1953.

Books that deal with topological groups, but with special emphases, include

C. Chevalley, *Theory of Lie Groups*, I, Princeton, Princeton University Press, 1946.

W. H. Gottschalk and G. A. Hedlund, *Topological Dynamics* (AMS Colloquium Publications, volume 36), American Mathematical Society, Providence, 1955.

D. Montgomery and L. Zippin, *Topological Transformation Groups*, Interscience Publishers, New York, 1955.

Another book that is listed here for lack of a better place is

L. Gillman and M. Jerison, *Rings of Continuous Functions*, D. Van Nostrand, Princeton, 1960. Chapter 15 of this important book contains a systematic development of uniform space theory based on the concept of a pseudometric.

Functional Analysis. Still another blend of general topology with algebra appears in modern functional analysis, where the algebra tends to be linear or multilinear, and the objectives are general versions of certain topics in classical analysis, notably spectral theory. The three books listed next are just a small sample from the literature in this burgeoning field.

N. Dunford and J. T. Schwartz, *Linear Operators*, Interscience Publishers, New York, Part 1, 1958; Part 2, 1963.

G. Köthe, *Topologische Lineare Räume*, Springer-Verlag, Berlin, 1960.

A. E. Taylor, *Introduction to Functional Analysis*, John Wiley and Sons, New York, 1958.

Classical Analysis. Because many of the ideas of general topology originated in classical analysis, it is not surprising that many of them are now being used to reformulate and expand classical analysis itself. What is surprising is that there are so few monographs that emphasize this process. One that does is

G. T. Whyburn, *Topological Analysis*, Princeton University Press, Princeton, 1958. See also the same author's complementary paper, "Developments in Topological Analysis," *Fundamenta Mathematicae*, **50**, 305–318 (1962).

Geometry. The general topology used in recent works on geometry tends not to go beyond the theory of metric spaces and of mild generalizations of metric spaces. Two books that use general topology in this way are

L. M. Blumenthal, *Theory and Applications of Distance Geometry*, Clarendon Press, Oxford, 1953.

H. Hadwiger, *Altes und Neues über konvexe Körper*, Birkhäuser Verlag, Basel and Stuttgart, 1955.

answers to some of the exercises

Almost all the answers given here are incomplete; some of them are only bare hints. Their object is not so much to supply a complete set of model responses as to provide some aid for the student who, having given an exercise a fair try, cannot finish it or is unsure of his results. Nor are the answers indicated here always the only correct ones—problems that call for proofs typically can be solved in a variety of valid ways.

1. All sets are open in this topological space.

3. Use axiom (C) and the definition of an open set.

4. The statement is clearly true for the case of one neighborhood; Hausdorff's axiom (B) takes care of the case of two neighborhoods; finish by mathematical induction.

5. (a) Neither (O_1) nor (O_2) is satisfied. (c) Condition (O_1) is not satisfied because $\emptyset$ does not belong to the collection. (e) Condition (O_3) is not satisfied.

6. Some samples: $\{\emptyset, \{a\}, \{a, c\}, S\}$; $\{\emptyset, \{a\}, \{b\}, \{b, c\}, S\}$; $\{\emptyset, \{a\}, \{a, b\}, \{a, c\}, S\}$.

7. Use one of De Morgan's formulas (*Sets*, 17) to verify (O_2).

8. Use the definitions and the fact that any subset of a finite set is finite.

9. $\Im$ is the discrete topology.

10. Use (N_2) and mathematical induction, as in Exercise 4.

12. The verification of (N_2) may serve as a specimen. If $x \prec X$ and $x \prec Y$, then there exist positive integers m and n such that $\{x + k2^m : k \in Z\} \subset X$ and $\{x + k2^n : k \in Z\} \subset Y$. If p is the larger of the numbers m and n, then

$$\{x + k2^p : k \in Z\} \subset X \cap Y,$$

so $x \prec X \cap Y$.

14. It is a particular case of the observation on p. 19 that if $x \in C(y, \beta)$, then there exists an α such that $C(x, \alpha) \subset C(y, \beta)$.

15. The sets (a), (c), and (d) are open; the others are not.

17. One such collection is the collection of all 2-cells centered at $(0, 0)$ whose radii are greater than 1.

19. The sets (b) and (d) are closed; the others are not.

20. Let $z \notin D(x, \alpha)$; then

$$(z_1 - x_1)^2 + \cdots + (z_n - x_n)^2 = \beta^2,$$

where $\beta > \alpha$; then by the inequality on p. 20, $C(x, \beta - \alpha) \subset CD(x, \alpha)$. Thus the latter set is open, so $D(x, \alpha)$ is closed.

23. Show that $C(\cup \alpha)$ is open, using the assumption of local finiteness and (G_2).

26. For (K_6), use the fact that $A \subset B$ if and only if $B = A \cup C$ for some set C.

27. One example may be constructed by taking $\mathfrak{X}$ to be the collection of all sets in R^1 of the form $\{x : 0 < x < b\}$, where $b > 0$, and using Exercise 25.

29. Only (K_3) is not satisfied; the offending set is $\{c\}$.

30. (a) $\emptyset$; (c) $\{0\}$; (d) R^1.

36. For (a), the interior is the set itself; the exterior is $\{(x, y) : x > 0\}$; and the boundary is $\{(x, y) : x = 0\}$.

37. Only (e).

39. For example, x is a boundary point of X if there are points of both X and CX arbitrarily close to x (see Exercise 47).

42. Suppose that $x \notin X' \cup Y'$. Then there exist neighborhoods N_1 and N_2 of x such that $N_1 \cap X = \emptyset$, $N_2 \cap Y = \emptyset$. Then $N = N_1 \cap N_2$ is a neighborhood of x disjoint from $X \cup Y$, so $x \notin (X \cup Y)'$. This shows that $(X \cup Y)' \subset X' \cup Y'$. The opposite inclusion follows from Exercise 41.

48. This follows from the definition of $b(X)$, one of De Morgan's formulas, and Exercise 46.

51. By Exercise 48, $b(X) = \overline{X} \cap C(X^\circ)$. Therefore $X - b(X) = X \cap Cb(X) = X \cap (C\overline{X} \cup X^\circ) = (X \cap C\overline{X}) \cup (X \cap X^\circ) = \emptyset \cup (X \cap X^\circ) = X^\circ$.

54. If X is dense and open, $CX = \overline{CX}$. Therefore, by Exercise 52, $(\overline{CX})^\circ = (CX)^\circ = C\overline{X} = CS = \emptyset$.

57. Use Theorem 5 and the fact that if N is a neighborhood of a point x of X, so is $X \cap N$.

61. $f(a) = a$.

62. One can use the functions f_x defined by $f_x(x) = 1$, $f_x(y) = 0$ if $y \neq x$.

65. The criterion is that $f(X') \subset [f(X)]'$ for every subset X of S_1. Exercise 43 and *Sets*, 27, can be used in the justification.

71. There are eight topological types.

74. (a) $\{\{a\}\}$; (c) $\{\{a, b\}, \{a, c\}\}$.

77. (a) The discrete topology; (c) the standard topology.

80. The most workable criterion is: If X belongs to either of the two bases and $x \in X$, then there exists a member Y of the other base such that $x \in Y \subset X$. Another is: Every member of either base is the union of some subcollection of the other.

82. It is different from both because, for example, the set $\{x: 0 \le x < 1\}$ belongs to the given topology but not to the standard topology, and any singleton belongs to the discrete topology but not to the given topology.

87. The induced topology is the standard topology.

89. (a) The trivial topology.

90. (a) The discrete topology; (b) the collection of all subsets of the set that are members of the standard topology on R^1.

92. The simplest way may be to show that every such subspace is homeomorphic to R^1.

96. It helps to think of the coordinates of the typical point of one C as $(\cos \varphi, \sin \varphi)$, and of those of the typical point of the other C as $(\cos \vartheta, \sin \vartheta)$, and to use the function from $C \times C$ onto the torus that is suggested by this choice.

98. This boils down to showing that between any two distinct real numbers there is one that does not belong to T.

100. If X is an equivalence class (that is, $X \in S/E$), then all elements of X have the same second "component," say y. The function $g: S/E \to R_1$ defined by $g(X) = y$ is a homeomorphism.

103. $0 < d(b, c) \le 2$.

107. If $\mathfrak{I}_1$ and $\mathfrak{I}_2$ are the natural topologies for the metrics d_1 and d_2 respectively, then their supremum is the natural topology for the metric d defined by $d(x, y) = \sup [d_1(x, y), d_2(x, y)]$.

108. To verify (M_3) use the inequality cited on p. 20.

113. Again, use the inequality cited on p. 20.

117. There are simple finite topological spaces with this property.

121. If $y \notin \{x: f(x) = g(x)\}$, then $f(y) = z \ne w = g(y)$. Let U and V be open sets separating $\{z\}$ and $\{w\}$; then y belongs to the open set $f^{-1}(U) \cap g^{-1}(V)$, which is disjoint from $\{x: f(x) = g(x)\}$.

122. The problem in each case is to construct an open cover that contains no finite cover.

125. In two cases the set in question is not closed.

126. Use finite spaces.

127. Use Theorem 22.

132. The most serious fault of the topology is that the concept of convergence to which it leads may not be the same as the given one.

135. Use the fact (which itself requires proof) that in a Hausdorff space, a sequence converges if its range is nonclosed, is finite, or has a nondiscrete relative topology.

138. Use the function f defined by $f(x) = \delta_d(\{x\}, X)$. Its continuity follows from the fact, which can be proved by way of (M_3) and Theorem 32, that $|f(x) - f(y)| \leq d(x, y)$. (The statement is still true if "compact" is replaced by "closed," and the proof becomes only slightly more difficult.)

139. The proof of Theorem 23 may provide a clue.

149. (b) The four sets may be taken to be $\emptyset$, S, and the two members of any disconnecting partition.

152. Recall Exercise 98, and use the easily verified fact that if r is any real number, the set $R^1 - \{r\}$ is disconnected in R^1.

156. One way is to show that the 2-sphere is arcwise connected by explicitly constructing an arc through any two given points. A second way is to show that the 2-sphere is homeomorphic to a certain quotient space obtained from a square. There are other ways.

160. The key observation is that $V_{r_1} V_{r_2} = V_r$, where r is the smaller of r_1 and r_2.

161. The simplest unnecessary property of metrics in this context is the part of (M_1) that says that $d(x, y) = 0$ only if $x = y$.

163. Use Theorem 43.

165. The materials for an answer to this exercise appear in previous examples and exercises.

168. Both are discrete.

175. Use Theorem 22.

179. (a), (b), and (d).

180. For the second part: $f(x) = x^{\frac{1}{3}}$ defines one such function.

181. In the language of calculus, they are the functions f such that $f(x) \to 0$ as $x \to +\infty$.

185. Take the supremum of the collection of uniformities compatible with $\mathfrak{I}$.

186. Use the remark just preceding Exercise 176.

189. Recall Theorem 51.

190. The necessary functions f can be defined in terms of the metric, somewhat in the manner of Exercise 138.

191. Prove and then use the fact that Δ is compact in the product space.

192. (b) gives the only convergent filter.

195. Theorem 20 can be used here.

201. Consider the filter generated by the collection of all sets of the form $\{x: \alpha < x < \beta\}$, where α and β are positive and $\alpha^2 < 2 < \beta^2$.

index of special symbols

C (complement of), 29, 146
$C(x, \alpha)$ (open cell in Euclidean space, or open ball in metric space, of center x and radius α), 19, 65
Δ (diagonal set), 105
i_X (identity map on X), 147
$\mathcal{P}(X)$ (power set of X), 144
R (the set of real numbers), 19
R^n (Cartesian product of n copies of R, or Euclidean n-space), 19, 21
$\bar{X}$ (closure of X), 25
X' (derived set of X), 30
X° (interior of X), 33
Z (set of all integers), 13

Z^+ (set of all positive integers), 28
$\emptyset$ (empty set), 144
$\twoheadleftarrow$ (has as a neighborhood), 13
$\subset$ (is contained in), 144
$\in$ (is an element of), 143
$\notin$ (is not an element of), 144
$\cap$ (intersection), 145
$\cup$ (union), 145
$\times$ (Cartesian product), 146, 148
$\{x \in X: \ldots x \ldots \}$ (set builder), 144
$(y_x : x \in X)$ (family with index set X), 148

general index